CALIFORNIA World History

Medieval and Early Modern Times

myWorld
INTERACTIVE
Active Journal

SAVVAS
LEARNING COMPANY

ISBN-13: 978-0-32-896016-3
ISBN-10:   0-32-896016-0

13 20

CONTENTS

CONTENTS

. . . .

Topic 4
The Islamic World and South Asia (610–1550)

CONTENTS

Topic 5
Civilizations of East Asia and Southeast Asia
(250 BCE—1644 CE)

Topic 6
Civilizations of the Americas (Prehistory–1533 CE)

CONTENTS

Topic 9
Global Convergence (1415–1763)

CONTENTS

Topic 10
Absolutism and Enlightenment (1516–1796)

x

TOPIC 1

The Roman and Byzantine Empires Preview

Essential Question **What forces can cause a society to change?**

Before you begin this topic, think about the Essential Question by answering the following question.

1. What are some ways that your community has changed over time? List three ways in which you have seen people, businesses, and other elements of society change.

Timeline Skills

As you read, write and/or draw at least three events from the topic. Draw a line from each event to its correct position on the timeline.

250 BCE	1 CE	250 CE

Map Skills

Using maps throughout the topic, label the outline map with the places listed. Then, color in the territory ruled by the Roman empire.

Byzantium   Rome   Jerusalem   Mediterranean Sea

Black Sea   Rhine River   Danube River   Anatolia

Egypt   Greece   Gaul   Spain

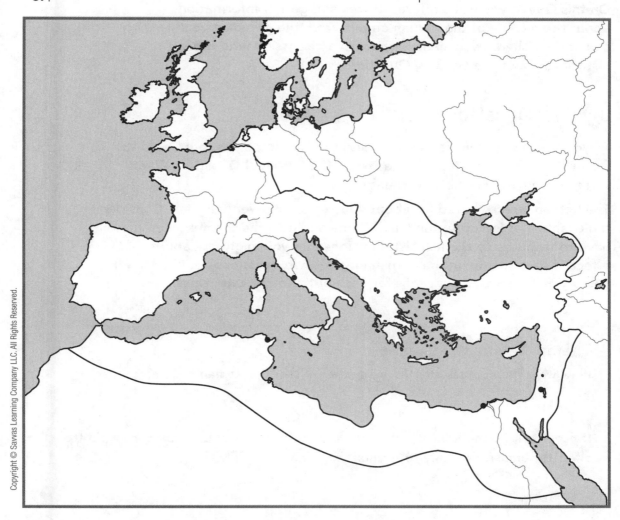

500 CE	1000 CE	1250 CE	1500 CE

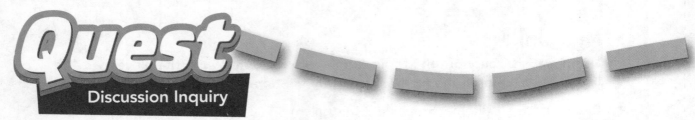

Quest
Discussion Inquiry

The Fall of Rome

On this Quest, you will explore sources and gather information about the decline of the Roman empire from the perspective of a historian. Then, you will participate in a discussion with other historians about the Guiding Question.

1 Ask Questions (See Student Text, page 10)

As you begin your Quest, keep in mind the Guiding Question: **Could the fall of Rome have been prevented?** and the Essential Question: **What forces can cause a society to change?**

The Roman empire lasted for about 450 years, but eventually fell. Consider the events that led up to the fall of Rome and how the themes listed may have contributed to the fall. List questions that you might ask about the effect of each theme on the Roman empire. Two questions are filled in for you. Add at least two questions for each of the other categories.

Theme Economic Weakness

How were trade routes affected by fighting within the Roman empire?

If people within the Roman empire could not afford to pay their taxes, how did that affect the emperor's ability to maintain an army?

Theme Political Conflict

Theme Political Corruption

Theme Social Conflict

Theme Invasions from Outside

Theme My Additional Questions

 INTERACTIVE

For extra help with Step 1, review the
21st Century Skills Tutorial: **Ask Questions**.

Quest CONNECTIONS

2 Investigate

As you read about the decline of the Roman empire, collect five connections from your text to answer the Guiding Question. Three connections are already chosen for you.

Connect to Augustus

Primary Source Augustus, *The Deeds of the Divine Augustus*
(See Student Text, page 18)

Here's a connection! Consider the list of great deeds that Augustus wrote about himself. What evidence can you find that Augustus was concerned about maintaining the strength of the empire?

Considering he was one of the greatest of Rome's emperors, why do you think Augustus found it necessary to write a long list of the things he had done?

Connect to Satire and Biography

Lesson 4 In-text Primary Source Juvenal's *Satire 10* (See Student Text, page 37)

What does this connection tell you about what Roman citizens were thinking about during times of trouble?

How do you think the Roman citizenry's attitude toward the government affected the empire's stability?

Connect to Economic Problems Worsen

Lesson 5 What was the Imperial Crisis? (See Student Text, page 42)

Here's another connection! Read the description of inflation in your text. What does the description tell you about the value of the Roman coins over time?

What does that indicate about what was happening to the Roman economy?

It's Your Turn! **Find two more connections. Fill in the title of your connections, then answer the questions. Connections may be images, primary sources, maps, or text.**

Your Choice | Connect to

Location in text

What is the main idea of this connection?

What does it tell you about the decline of the Roman empire? Could it have been prevented?

Your Choice | Connect to

Location in text

What is the main idea of this connection?

What does it tell you about the decline of the Roman empire? Could it have been prevented?

③ Examine Sources (See Student Text, page 58)

Examine the secondary sources provided online or from your teacher. Fill in the chart to note the viewpoints of four historians on the question of whether Rome's fall could have been prevented. The first one is completed for you.

Could the fall of Rome have been prevented?	
Source	Yes or No? Why?
The Decline and Fall of the Roman Empire	NO, because the empire was too big to support.
The Day of the Barbarians	
History of the Later Roman Empire	
The Fall of the Roman Empire	

> 👆 **INTERACTIVE**
>
> For extra help with Step 3, review the 21st Century Skills Tutorial: **Compare Viewpoints**.

Quest FINDINGS

4 Discuss! (See Student Text, page 58)

Now that you have collected connections and explored documents about the fall of the Roman empire, you are ready to discuss with your fellow historians the Guiding Question: **Could the fall of Rome have been prevented?** Follow the steps below, using the spaces provided to prepare for your discussion.

You will work with a partner in a small group of historians. Try to reach consensus, a situation in which everyone is in agreement, on the question. Can you do it?

1. **Prepare Your Arguments** You will be assigned a position on the question, either YES or NO.

   My position: ....

   Work with your partner to review your Quest notes from the Quest Connections and Quest Sources.

   - If you were assigned YES, agree with your partner on what you think were the strongest arguments from Bury and Grant.
   - If you were assigned NO, agree on what you think were the strongest arguments from Gibbon and Barbero.

2. **Present Your Position** Those assigned YES will present their arguments and evidence first. As you listen, ask clarifying questions to gain information and understanding.

What is a Clarifying Question?	
These types of questions do not judge the person talking. They are only for the listener to be clear on what he or she is hearing.	
Example: Can you tell me more about that?	Example: You said [x]. Am I getting that right?

INTERACTIVE

For extra help with Step 4, review the 21st Century Skills Tutorial: **Participate in a Discussion or Debate**.

While the opposite side speaks, take notes on what you hear in the space below.

```
. . . . . . . . . . . . . . . . . . . . . . . . . . . . . . . . . . . . .
.                                                                       .
.                                                                       .
.                                                                       .
.                                                                       .
.                                                                       .
.                                                                       .
.                                                                       .
. . . . . . . . . . . . . . . . . . . . . . . . . . . . . . . . . . . . .
```

3. **Switch!** Now NO and YES will switch sides. If you argued YES before, now you will argue NO. Work with your same partner and use your notes. Add any arguments and evidence from the clues and sources. Those *now* arguing YES go first.

When both sides have finished, answer the following:

Before I started this discussion with my fellow historians, my opinion was that	*After* I started this discussion with my fellow historians, my opinion was that
_____the fall of Rome could have been prevented. _____the fall of Rome could not have been prevented.	_____the fall of Rome could have been prevented. _____the fall of Rome could not have been prevented.

4. **Point of View** Do you all agree on the answer to the Guiding Question?

_____ Yes

_____ No

If not, on what points do you all agree?

```
. . . . . . . . . . . . . . . . . . . . . . . . . . . . . . . . . . . . .
.                                                                       .
.                                                                       .
.                                                                       .
.                                                                       .
.                                                                       .
.                                                                       .
.                                                                       .
. . . . . . . . . . . . . . . . . . . . . . . . . . . . . . . . . . . . .
```

Take Notes

Literacy Skills: Analyze Cause and Effect Use what you have read to complete the table. Factors that helped the Roman empire grow appear in the left column. Record ways that those factors contributed to the empire's growth in the right column. One has been completed for you.

Causes	Effects
Rule by emperors	ended civil wars; brought peace; made the empire more stable for a time; began the Pax Romana
Pax Romana	
Rome's practical achievements	
Roman military	
Roman trade and economic activity	

INTERACTIVE

For extra help, review the 21st Century Skills Tutorial: **Analyze Cause and Effect**.

Practice Vocabulary

Sentence Builder Finish the sentences below with a vocabulary term from this section. You may have to change the form of the words to complete the sentences.

Word Bank

aqueduct   concrete

deify   Pax Romana

1. Emperors who are officially declared to be gods have been

2. Romans experienced a long period of peace and prosperity during the

3. Mixing stone and sand with limestone, clay, and water produces a useful building material called

4. Roman cities grew rapidly, partly because engineers brought water great distances through

Quick Activity Where Do They Go Next?

The Roman empire reached its greatest territorial extent under Emperor Trajan who ruled from 98 CE to 117 CE. With a partner, study the map of the Roman empire and what surrounded its borders in 117 CE.

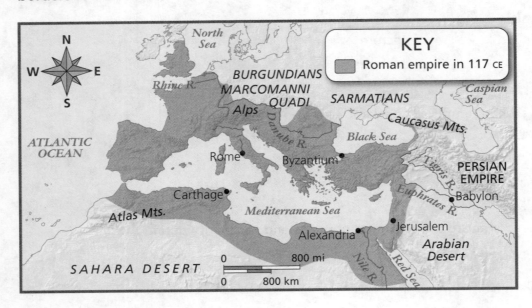

Team Challenge! You probably noticed that the Roman empire expanded across a large area of southern Europe, North Africa, and parts of southwestern Asia. What lands were left to conquer? Where could the Romans go next? What physical features, peoples, or empires lie at the empire's northern, southern, eastern, and western borders? Form a group with three other students. In your group, answer the question: Why did the Roman empire fail to expand after 117 CE? Write your responses on sticky notes, and add them to the class board.

Take Notes

Literacy Skills: Sequence Use what you have read to complete the timeline. Record what happened on each of the dates listed. Then connect each box to the timeline at the appropriate spot. One has been completed for you.

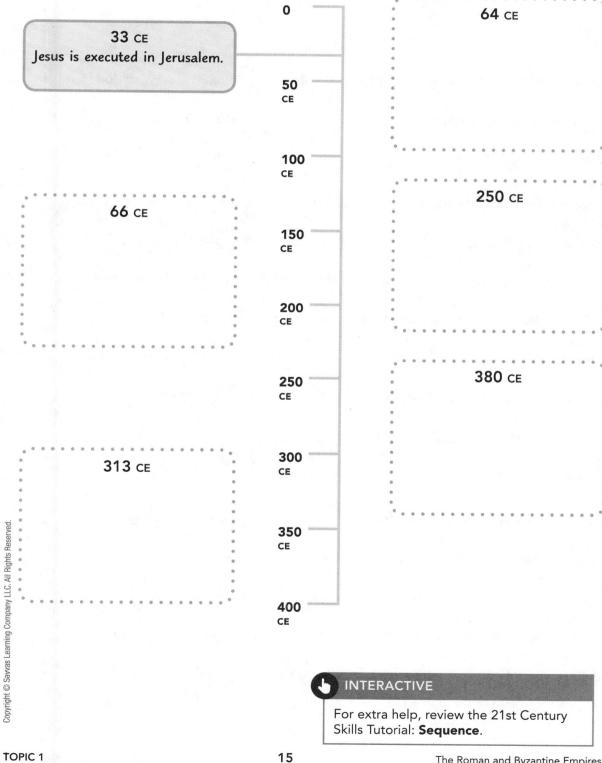

33 CE
Jesus is executed in Jerusalem.

0

50 CE

100 CE

66 CE

150 CE

200 CE

250 CE

300 CE

313 CE

350 CE

400 CE

64 CE

250 CE

380 CE

👆 **INTERACTIVE**

For extra help, review the 21st Century Skills Tutorial: **Sequence**.

Practice Vocabulary

Word Bank Choose one word from the word bank to fill in each blank. When you have finished, you will have a short summary of important ideas from the section.

Word Bank

baptism	conversion	crucifixion
martyr	resurrection	

Christianity began in Judea, then part of the Roman empire. The Jews of Judea practiced many religious traditions, including a ritual plunging into water, which was later adopted by Christianity as the rite of ....

According to Christian tradition, Jesus of Nazareth preached ideas from the Hebrew Bible and added other ideas about how to live a good life. Many people began to believe that Jesus was the Messiah. As more and more people followed Jesus, the Roman government saw Jesus as a threat and had him executed by .... Some of Jesus' followers said that they saw him again after his death. These believers helped form a new religion called Christianity. They believed that Jesus' .... was proof that he was the Messiah.

After Jesus' death, some of his followers worked to spread his teachings. One was Paul, who opposed Christianity until he experienced a .... that changed his views. As Christianity spread, many Roman emperors responded with persecution. Many Christians died for their beliefs. A person who dies for his or her beliefs is called a ....

Take Notes

Literacy Skills: Analyze Text Structure Use what you have read to complete the outline. The items listed below reflect the headings and subheadings in the lesson. Record key details beneath the headings. The first one has been completed for you.

I. The Christian Bible
 A. The Old and New Testaments
  1. The Old Testament comprises the scriptures of the Hebrew Bible.
  2. The New Testament comprises 27 documents, called *books*, added by Christians.
 B. What Are the Gospels?

 C. Teachings in Other Books

II. What Do Christians Believe About God?
 A. The Son of God

 B. The Soul and Salvation

 C. The Trinity

III. Practicing Christianity
 A. Following Jesus' Teachings

 B. Christianity Today

 C. Christian Rituals and Holidays

IV. What Is the Judeo-Christian tradition?

 INTERACTIVE

For extra help, review the 21st Century Skills Tutorial: **Organize Your Ideas**.

Practice Vocabulary

Vocabulary Quiz Show Some quiz shows ask a question and expect the contestant to give the answer. In other shows, the contestant is given an answer and must supply the question. If the blank is in the Question column, write the question that would result in the answer in the Answer column. If the question is supplied, write the answer.

Question	Answer
1. What text makes up the second part of the Christian Bible, and is not part of the Hebrew Bible?	1.
2.	2. epistles
3.	3. Trinity
4. What stories did Jesus often use to teach important lessons?	4.
5. What are large groups within Christianity that share certain beliefs and rituals, but disagree on others?	5.
6.	6. Gospel
7. What subject deals with issues of right and wrong and the best way to treat people?	7.

Take Notes

Literacy Skills: Identify Main Ideas and Details Use what you have read to complete the concept web. Record details about each aspect of Roman culture under the empire. The first one has been completed for you.

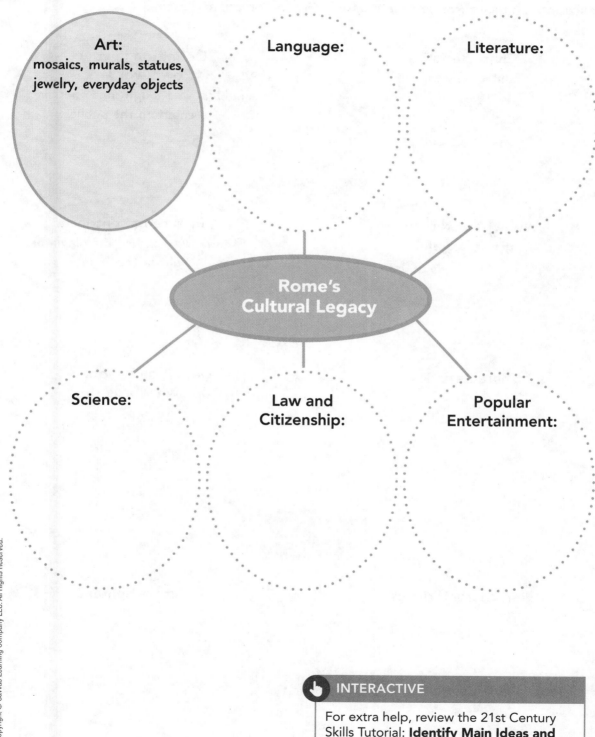

Art: mosaics, murals, statues, jewelry, everyday objects

Language:

Literature:

Rome's Cultural Legacy

Science:

Law and Citizenship:

Popular Entertainment:

👆 INTERACTIVE

For extra help, review the 21st Century Skills Tutorial: **Identify Main Ideas and Details**.

Practice Vocabulary

Word Map Study the word map for the word *gladiator*. Characteristics are words or phrases that relate to the word in the center of the word map. Non-characteristics are words and phrases not associated with the word. Use the blank word map to explore the meaning of the word *oratory*. Then make word maps of your own for these words: *site of encounter, mosaic, Romance languages, Greco-Roman,* and *satire*.

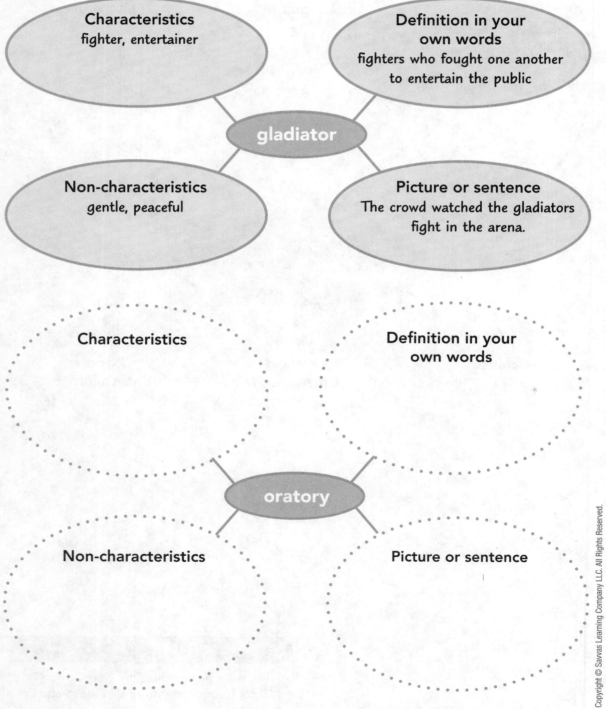

Characteristics
fighter, entertainer

Definition in your own words
fighters who fought one another to entertain the public

gladiator

Non-characteristics
gentle, peaceful

Picture or sentence
The crowd watched the gladiators fight in the arena.

Characteristics

Definition in your own words

oratory

Non-characteristics

Picture or sentence

Take Notes

Literacy Skills: Analyze Cause and Effect Use what you have read to complete the chart. Record specific events and their effects that contributed to the decline of the Roman empire.

Cause	Event	Effect
Marcus Aurelius dies.		Pax Romana ends.
Civil wars erupt.	Inflation grows. Trade networks are disrupted. Foreign invasions advance.	
Diocletian tries to stabilize Rome.		Military leaders fight for power.
Theodosius dies.		Rome falls.

INTERACTIVE

For extra help, review the 21st Century Skills Tutorial: **Analyze Cause and Effect**.

Practice Vocabulary

Words in Context For each question below, write an answer that shows your understanding of the **boldfaced** key term.

1. What are problems that people might have in a time of **inflation**?

2. According to the Romans, why were the Germans **barbarians**?

3. How did Emperor Theodosius show his support for Christian **orthodoxy**?

4. What role did **mercenaries** play in the Roman empire's fight to survive?

Quick Activity Did the Roman Empire Fall?

Read the excerpt below. Discuss with a partner what the excerpt suggests about the "fall" of the western Roman empire.

> "Nations innumerable and most savage have invaded all Gaul. The Whole region between the Alps and the Pyrenees, the ocean and the Rhine, has been devastated … Oh wretched Empire! … Who could believe that Rome, built upon the conquest of the whole world, would fall to the ground?"
>
> —*St. Jerome on the Germanic Invasions, 409* C.E.

In 476 CE, Germanic invaders overthrew the last Roman emperor in the western empire, Romulus. The city of Rome fell. Meanwhile, to the east, the Byzantine empire continued and even thrived. Not until 1453 did the Ottoman Turks capture the Byzantine capital of Constantinople. Historians often refer to the end of the western Roman empire as the "fall" of the Roman empire. Some argue that the empire did not fall, however. They maintain that the empire broke down slowly, over a long period of time, and that Roman civilization continued in the east as the Byzantine empire, up until 1453. Use what you have learned in the lessons to discuss, in a small group, the causes of the decline of the western Roman empire as well as the ways in which Roman civilization continued.

Team Challenge! Take a Thumb Vote in response to the question **Did the Roman empire fall?** Organize into groups based on your votes. With your new group, write a paragraph that answers the question and provides at least two pieces of evidence to support your position. If you answer "yes," explain why *fall* is an appropriate description, despite suggestions that Roman civilization continued beyond 476 CE. If you answer "no," explain why *fall* is wrong and suggest an alternative word or phrase as a more appropriate description.

Take Notes

Literacy Skills: Use Evidence Use what you have read to complete the table. Record the main idea for each heading in the lesson. Then, list evidence to support the main idea. The first one has been completed for you.

Main Idea	Evidence
What Was the New Rome? The Eastern Roman, or Byzantine, empire grew around a new political and economic center.	• Constantine established the capital of the Eastern Roman empire at Constantinople, on the site of Byzantium. • Located on the Bosporous Strait, Constantinople became a center for trade and was easier to defend than Rome.
Who Were Justinian and Theodora?	• •
The Shrinking Empire	• •
The Empire's Influence	• •
Early Russia	• •

Practice Vocabulary

Sentence Revision Revise each sentence so that the underlined vocabulary word is used logically. Be sure not to change the vocabulary word. The first one is done for you.

1. The <u>Byzantine</u> empire was named after Emperor Constantine.

    The <u>Byzantine</u> empire was so named because its capital, Constantinople, was built at a place once called Byzantium.

2. A <u>strait</u> is a wide body of water surrounding an island.

3. The <u>moat</u> was a trench filled with stones.

4. <u>Greek fire</u> was a liquid that quickly stopped flames from spreading.

5. A <u>missionary</u> generally lacked the confidence to promote his religion.

6. The <u>Cyrillic alphabet</u> was used by the Romans.

Take Notes

Literacy Skills: Compare and Contrast Use what you have read to complete the chart. List features that the Roman Catholic Church and the Eastern Orthodox Church share, as well as features that make each church unique. One has been completed for you.

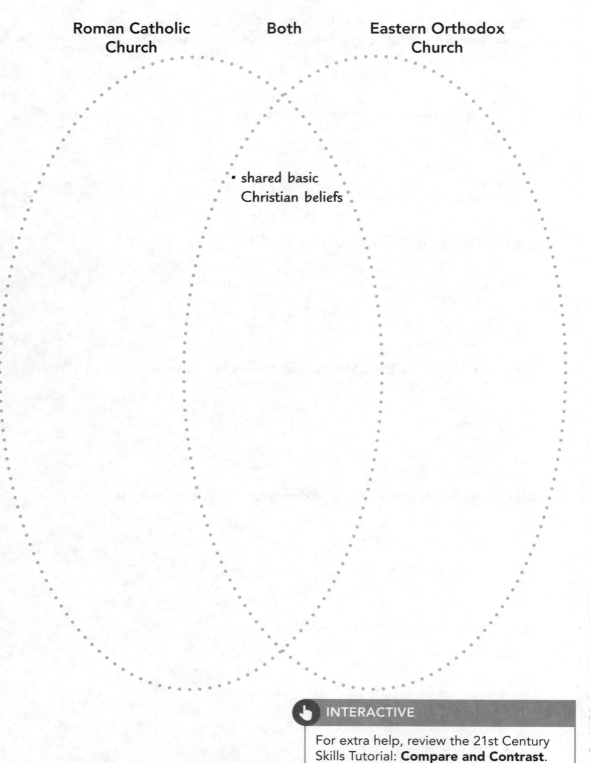

Roman Catholic Church   Both   Eastern Orthodox Church

• shared basic Christian beliefs

INTERACTIVE

For extra help, review the 21st Century Skills Tutorial: **Compare and Contrast**.

Practice Vocabulary

Sentence Builder **Finish the sentences below with a key term from this section. You may have to change the form of the words to complete the sentences.**

Word Bank

creed   Great Schism   icon

iconoclast   Justinian's Code   pope

1. Church leadership was the most important issue between Eastern Orthodox and Roman Catholic churches in the

....

2. The leader of the Roman Catholic Church was the

....

3. Many Christians believed it was wrong to worship holy images called

....

4. The Byzantine empire and its emperor benefited from the unified body of law organized under

....

5. In 325, Church officials prepared a clear statement of beliefs, or

....

6. Byzantines who destroyed holy images in churches were called

....

Writing Workshop Arguments

As you read, build a response to this question: Which civilization was greater, the Greek city-states or the Roman empire? The prompts below will help walk you through the process.

Lessons 1 and 2 Writing Tasks: Introduce Claims and Gather Details
(See Student Text, pages 17 and 25)

In this topic, you will write an argument on the question: Which was greater, the Greek city-states or the Roman empire? Consider the following factors: size, longevity, economic power, cultural achievements, and influence. Add facts about each civilization to this chart.

Factor	Greece	Rome	Advantage? (G/R)
Size			
Longevity			
Economic Power			
Culture Achievements			

Lesson 3 Writing Task: Use Credible Sources (See Student Text, page 31)

On a separate sheet of paper, list at least three print or digital sources, other than your text, that you will use to check your conclusions.

Lesson 4 Writing Task: Introduce a Claim (See Student Text, page 40)

Look at your chart and mark which civilization had the advantage in each area in your opinion. From this exercise, can you choose which civilization you think was greater? If you can't support choosing one, argue that they both have claims to greatness. Form your conclusion into a one-sentence statement and write it in the outline.

Lessons 5 and 6 Writing Tasks: Support a Claim and Distinguish Claims from Opposing Claims (See Student Text, pages 45 and 51)

Make an outline of your essay, listing your best examples of why one society might be greater than the other and an opposing claim.

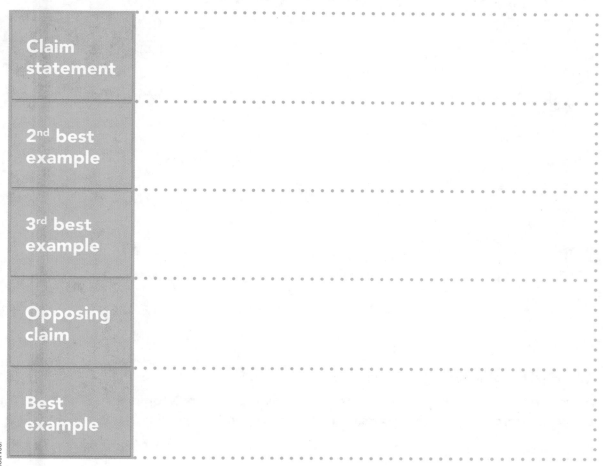

Claim statement	
2nd best example	
3rd best example	
Opposing claim	
Best example	

Lesson 7 Writing Task: Shape Tone (See Student Text, page 57)

As your write, use phrases such as "clearly" or "in fact," to emphasize your points, and phrases such as "on the other hand," or "in contrast" to introduce an opposing claim.

Writing Task (See Student Text, page 59)

Using the outline you created, answer the following question in a five-paragraph argument: Which was greater, the Greek city-states or the Roman empire?

👆 **INTERACTIVE**

For extra help, review the 21st Century Skills Tutorials: **Support Ideas with Evidence** and **Consider and Counter Opposing Arguments**.

Life in Medieval Christendom Preview

Essential Question How did societies preserve order?

Before you begin this topic, think about the Essential Question by answering the following question.

1. What are some ways that people and institutions keep order and prevent conflict in your community? Work with a partner to brainstorm five ideas. List them below. Circle the two that you think are the most important or effective.

Timeline Skills

As you read, write and/or draw at least three events from the topic. Draw a line from each event to its correct position on the timeline.

500 CE	750 CE

Map Skills

Using maps throughout the topic, label the outline map with the places listed. Then color in bodies of water, mountain ranges, and plains.

Alps	Atlantic Ocean	Balkan Peninsula
Black Sea	Caspian Sea	Iberian Peninsula
Italian Peninsula	Mediterranean Sea	North European Plain
North Sea	Scandinavian Peninsula	Ural Mountains

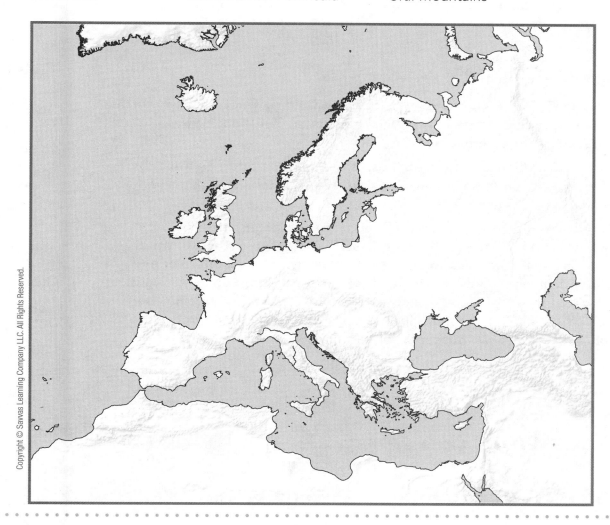

1000 CE	1250 CE

Quest
Discussion Inquiry

Freedom vs. Security?

On this Quest, you will explore sources and gather information about the relationships that existed under feudalism. Then, you will participate in a civic discussion about the Guiding Question.

1 Ask Questions (See Student Text, page 64)

As you begin your Quest, keep in mind the Guiding Question: **Is it worth trading freedom for security?** and the Essential Question: **How do societies preserve order?**

The word *order* has many meanings. In this sense, it refers to freedom from violence and unruly behavior, or peace and stability within and among communities.

During the Middle Ages, Europe faced many challenges, including invaders and lawlessness. To meet these challenges, a system known as feudalism emerged. This system relied on the interdependent roles and responsibilities of lords, vassals, and serfs. List questions that you might ask about these roles and responsibilities with regard to different aspects of life. Two questions for the first theme are filled in for you. Add at least two questions for each additional theme.

Theme Defense and Security

Sample questions:

How did lords provide defense for the people under their protection?

What did lords expect in exchange for this protection?

Theme Economic Activity

Theme Government and Law

Theme Social Relations

Theme Religion and Culture

Theme My Additional Questions

INTERACTIVE

For extra help with Step 1, review the 21st Century Tutorial: **Ask Questions**.

Quest CONNECTIONS

② Investigate

As you read about medieval Europe, collect five connections from your text to help you answer the Guiding Question. Three connections are already chosen for you.

Connect to Charlemagne

Primary Source Einhard, *The Life of Charlemagne* (See Student Text, page 70)

Here's a connection! Read the description of Charlemagne, King of the Franks. What does the text describe the king doing? What does it show about life in medieval Europe, and the responsibilities of kings? How did medieval knights help provide security for lords and peasants?

What trade-offs do people at different levels of society make for security?

Connect to Feudalism

Lesson 3 Feudalism in Medieval Europe (See Student Text, page 81)

Here's another connection! Look at the diagram of feudalism and social relationships in your text. The king is at the top. What roles do the people on the other levels fulfill? How do they support the king and what do they get in exchange? How do these relationships preserve order in feudal society?

What trade-offs do people at different levels of society make for security?

Connect to the Medieval Manor

Lesson 3 How Did Medieval Manors Work? (See Student Text, page 83)

What does this diagram show you about the social structure that existed on medieval manors? How does this structure illustrate the relationship between serfs and their feudal lords?

What trade-offs do people at different levels of society make for security?

It's Your Turn! **Find two more connections. Fill in the title of your connections, then answer the questions. Connections may be images, primary sources, maps, or text.**

Your Choice | Connect to

Location in text

What is the main idea of this connection?

What does it tell you about how feudal roles and relationships provided for security in medieval Europe?

Your Choice | Connect to

Location in text

What is the main idea of this connection?

What does it tell you about how feudal roles and relationships provided for security in medieval Europe?

③ Examine Sources (See Student Text, page 100)

Examine the primary and secondary sources provided online or from your teacher. Fill in the chart to show what these sources suggest about the trade-off of freedom for security in today's world. The first one is completed for you.

Is It Worth Trading Freedom for Security?	
Source	**Yes or No? Why?**
"Theresa May's Speech on Terrorism and Extremism"	YES, because there are certain responsibilities one has in a free society, such as respect for British laws.
"Hollande Seeks to Extend State of Emergency Despite Critics"	
"UN Rights Experts Urge France to Protect Fundamental Freedoms While Countering Terrorism"	

 INTERACTIVE

For extra help with Step 3, review the 21st Century Tutorials: **Compare Viewpoints** and **Analyze Primary and Secondary Sources**.

 **FINDINGS**

4 Discuss (See Student Text, page 100)

You have collected clues about life in medieval Europe and the relationships that existed under feudalism and explored documents about freedom and security in today's world. Now, you are ready to discuss with your classmates the Guiding Question: **Is it worth trading freedom for security?**

You will work with a partner in a small group. Try to reach consensus, a situation where everyone is in agreement, on the question.

1. **Prepare Your Arguments** You will be assigned a position on the question, either YES or NO.

My position: ....

Work with your partner to review your Quest notes from the Quest Connections and Quest Sources.

• If you were assigned YES, agree with your partner on what you think were the strongest arguments from May and Jacinto.

• If you were assigned NO, agree on what you think were the strongest arguments from the UN Rights Experts.

2. **Present Your Position** Those assigned YES will present their arguments and evidence first. As you listen, ask clarifying questions to gain information and understanding.

What is a Clarifying Question?	
These types of questions do not judge the person talking. They are only for the listener to be clear on what he or she is hearing.	
Example: Can you tell me more about that?	Example: You said [x]. Am I getting that right?

👆 **INTERACTIVE**

For extra help with Step 4, review the 21st Century Tutorial: **Participate in a Discussion or Debate**.

While the opposite side speaks, take notes on what you hear in the space below.

3. **Switch!** Now NO and YES will switch sides. If you argued YES before, now you will argue NO. Work with your same partner and use your notes. Add any arguments and evidence from the clues and sources. Those *now* arguing YES go first.

When both sides have finished, answer the following:

Before I started this discussion with my classmates, my opinion was that	After I started this discussion with my classmates, my opinion was that
____ it is worth trading freedom for security. ____ it is not worth trading freedom for security.	____ it is worth trading freedom for security. ____ it is not worth trading freedom for security.

4. **Point of View** Do you all agree on the answer to the Guiding Question?

- __ Yes
- __ No

If not, on what points do you all agree?

Take Notes

Literacy Skills: Sequence Use what you have read to complete the timeline. Draw a line from each event to its correct space on the timeline. Then, write a brief description of each event. The first one has been completed for you.

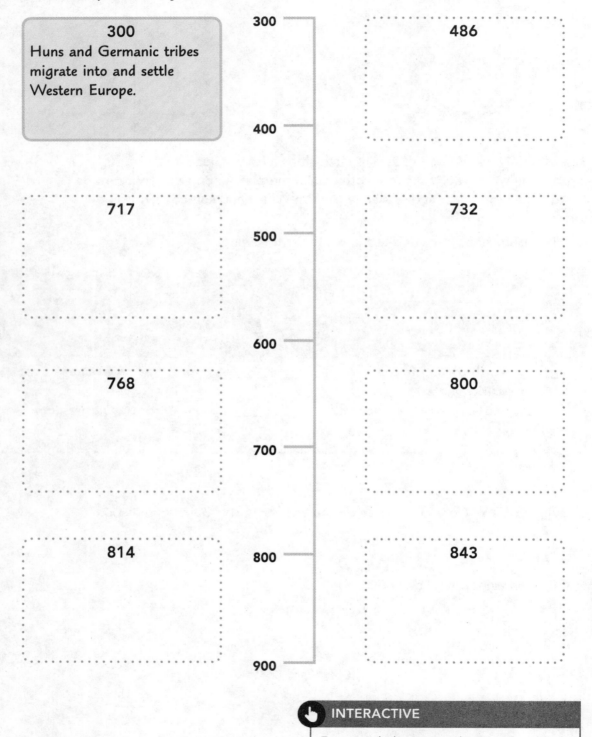

300
Huns and Germanic tribes migrate into and settle Western Europe.

300

486

400

717

732

500

600

768

800

700

814

843

800

900

INTERACTIVE

For extra help, review the 21st Century Tutorial: **Sequence**.

Practice Vocabulary

True or False? Decide whether each statement below is true or false. Circle T or F, and then explain your answer. Be sure to include the underlined vocabulary word in your explanation. The first one is done for you.

1. **T / F** The <u>Middle Ages</u> in Europe began with the rise of the western Roman empire.

   False; The <u>Middle Ages</u> in Europe began with the fall of the western Roman empire.

2. **T / F** Under Charlemagne, much of <u>medieval</u> civilization in Europe adopted Christianity.

3. **T / F** Pope Leo III strengthened the role of the Church and the <u>clergy</u> in Europe when he crowned Charlemagne emperor of the Romans.

4. **T / F** Europe has a generally flat and open <u>topography</u> that has left the continent vulnerable to invasion.

Quick Activity Traveling the Rhine

Study the map of the Rhine River and its major tributaries, or branch rivers, below. What do you notice about the river? How do you think the river encouraged the growth of medieval civilization in Western Europe? Discuss your ideas with a partner.

Did you know?

Estimates of the length of the Rhine River vary from 765 to 820 miles.

Several tributaries, including the Neckar and the Main, extend the reach of the Rhine by several hundred miles.

The Rhine River flows generally in a northwesterly direction.

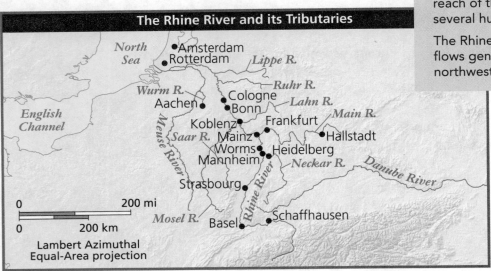

The Rhine River and its Tributaries

Team Challenge! In the classroom, the hallway, or another appropriate space, use masking tape to make a large model of the Rhine River and its major tributaries. Divide the class into a Towns group and a Directions group. Write the names of medieval towns on labels, and affix the labels to the backs of Towns students. Have the Directions students take turns guiding Towns students to the correct location on the map by answering questions, such as "Am I located downstream (in the direction the river flows) or upstream (in the opposite direction)? Am I on the Rhine or a tributary? Near what other town am I located?"

Take Notes

Literacy Skills: Summarize Use what you have read to complete the
chart. The column headings correspond to the headings in the text.
Summarize information for each section in the text as you read.
The first one has been completed for you.

How Did Europe Become Christian?	The Role of Monasteries and Convents	The Medieval Church
Patrick Converts Ireland In the 4th century, Patrick, a man sold into slavery went on to become a missionary who founded the first Catholic Church in Ireland and helped spread Christianity throughout the British Isles. For his work, the Church named him a saint.	**The Benedictine Rule**	**Catholic Teachings**
Missionaries Arrive in Britain	**Everyday Life in Monasteries**	**The Power of the Medieval Church**
Christianity Spreads Through Europe	**Primary Source**	**What Was Christendom?**

INTERACTIVE

For extra help, review the 21st Century
Tutorial: **Summarize**.

Practice Vocabulary

Matching Logic Using your knowledge of the underlined vocabulary words, draw a line from each sentence in Column 1 to match it with the sentence in Column 2 to which it logically belongs.

Column 1	Column 2
1. In the Early Middle Ages, many people across Europe remained <u>pagans</u>.	They converted many people and their rulers to Christianity.
2. Catholics believed that they must follow God's laws as the Church taught them and practice the <u>sacraments</u>.	Men followed a strict rule of life that balanced prayer and work.
3. The monk Benedict founded the first European <u>monastery</u> in 529.	They believed in many gods and goddesses.
4. Over the course of the Middle Ages, most of Europe came to view themselves as part of a wider <u>Christendom</u>.	He was believed to be especially holy because he founded the first Catholic Church in Ireland.
5. The Catholic Church recognized the work of a formerly enslaved man named Patrick by naming him a <u>saint</u>.	This large community of Christians extends beyond Europe to places all across the world.
6. Medieval popes sent <u>missionaries</u> to kingdoms and lands across Europe.	They joined the Church through baptism and consumed bread and wine that they believed became the body and blood of Christ through communion.
7. Some medieval women chose to devote themselves to the Catholic Church by entering <u>convents</u>.	They took vows similar to those of monks to seclude themselves in worship.

Take Notes

Literacy Skills: Identify Main Idea and Details Use what you have read to complete the table. In each column, write one main idea and three supporting details from each section of the text. The first one has been completed for you.

A Violent Time	How Did Feudal Society Provide Protection?	How Did Medieval Manors Work?
Main Idea: Between 800 and 1000, waves of invasions changed life in Western Europe.	**Main Idea:**	**Main Idea:**
Supporting Detail: Vikings invaded from the north, Muslims from the south, and Magyars from the south and east.	**Supporting Detail:**	**Supporting Detail:**
Supporting Detail:	**Supporting Detail:**	**Supporting Detail:**
Supporting Detail:	**Supporting Detail:**	**Supporting Detail:**

INTERACTIVE

For extra help, review the 21st Century Tutorial: **Identify Main Ideas and Details.**

Practice Vocabulary

Words in Context For each question below, write an answer that shows your understanding of the boldfaced key term.

1. In exchange for land, what did a **vassal** pledge to a more powerful lord?

2. What is the significance of a **fief** in the feudal system?

3. How did a young man become a **knight**?

4. What did **chivalry** require of a knight?

5. Why was the **manor** considered the heart of the medieval economy?

6. What standing did a **serf** have in medieval society?

Take Notes

Literacy Skills: Summarize Use what you have read to complete the table. Record important details from each section of the lesson to summarize change that took place during the Middle Ages. The first one has been completed for you.

New Ways of Farming	Trade and Industry	Growth of Towns
Plows with iron blades pulled by horses replace wooden plows pulled by oxen, so thicker soils of northern Europe could be worked faster.		

INTERACTIVE

For extra help, review the 21st Century Tutorial: **Summarize**.

Practice Vocabulary

Sentence Builder Finish the sentences below with a key term from this section. You may have to change the form of the words to complete the sentences.

Word Bank

crop rotation	fallow
three-field system	guild

1. Farmers planted spring crops, winter crops, and no crops in the

2. To allow the soil to recover some of its natural fertility, farmers every year left one field

3. The practice of changing the use of fields over time is known as

4. Workers who practiced the same craft joined together to protect their economic interests in a

Take Notes

Literacy Skills: Analyze Text Structure Use what you have read to complete the outline. List important details from each section, as well as text features like primary sources and infographics, in the lesson beneath the headings and subheadings. The first one has been completed for you.

Forms of Devotion	How Did Religion Affect Medieval Culture?	Why Did Learning Grow?
Religious Orders At first, monks and nuns prayed and meditated in remote monasteries. Later, monasteries became centers of agricultural production and were located in towns. Mendicant orders were founded to fight heresy and to preach to ordinary people in cities.	**Revival of Drama**	**Medieval Universities**
Francis and Clare	**New Architecture**	**Thomas Aquinas**
	The Church Shapes Chivalry	**An Age of Confidence**

👆 **INTERACTIVE**

For extra help, review the 21st Century Tutorial: **Summarize**.

Practice Vocabulary

Words in Context For each question below, write an answer that shows your understanding of the boldfaced key term.

1. How did **mendicant orders** help the people of the growing towns?

2. How did the Church influence the growth of **universities**?

3. How did Thomas Aquinas use **natural law** to explain that both faith and reason come from God?

Quick Activity Illuminating the Middle Ages

With a partner, examine these photos of medieval illuminated texts.

Did you notice the elaborate design and handwritten script of the two pages? During the Middle Ages skilled monks and others copied manuscripts by hand. These manuscripts were often illuminated, or illustrated, with pictures or designs. Most illuminations had religious themes. However, some depicted scenes of everyday life.

Team Challenge! Read the excerpts from Geoffrey Chaucer's The Canterbury Tales below. With your partner, select one of the passages and create your own illuminated text. Be sure to pick a design that fits the content of the excerpt.

The Knight

> A knight there was, and he a worthy man,
>
> Who, from the moment that he first began
>
> To ride about the world, loved chivalry,
>
> Truth, honour, freedom and all courtesy.
>
> Full worthy was he in his liege-lord's war,
>
> And therein had he ridden (none more far)
>
> As well in Christendom as heathenesse,
>
> And honoured everywhere for worthiness.

The Prioress

> There was also a nun, a prioress, . . .
>
> She was so charitable and piteous
>
> That she would weep if she but saw a mouse
>
> Caught in a trap, though it were dead or bled.
>
> She had some little dogs, too, that she fed
>
> On roasted flesh, or milk and fine white bread.
>
> But sore she'd weep if one of them were dead,
>
> Or if men smote it with a rod to smart:
>
> For pity ruled her, and her tender heart.
>
> — *Prologue from The Canterbury Tales, by Geoffrey Chaucer*

Writing Workshop Narrative

As you read, brainstorm ideas, gather information, and prepare to write diary entries from the perspective of three medieval figures—selecting from a knight, a serf, and a monk or nun. The prompts below will help walk you through the process.

Lesson 1 Writing Task: Use Credible Sources Consider the historical figures from whose perspective you can write. On a separate sheet of paper, list five sources other than the textbook that you could use to learn about the lives of these figures. Keep in mind that you can list primary and secondary sources. These can be text, visual, video, or audio.

Lesson 2 Writing Task: Identify Main Ideas In the chart, write two things that you think you know about each of the historical figures— knight, serf, monk, and nun—in the second column. Then, write a main idea that describes why you find each historical figure interesting. Which do you consider most interesting? Circle the three figures from whose perspective you will write.

	What Do I Know About This Person?	I Find Them Interesting Because . . .
knight		
serf		
monk		
nun		

Lesson 3 Writing Task: Use Narrative Techniques As you prepare to write, consider the tone and style of language each of the figures might use. Think about the types of figurative language, such as metaphors and similes, as well as the level of detail, formality, and emotion with which the figures might write. Pick one figure and write your thoughts on his or her tone and style of language on a separate sheet of paper.

Lesson 4 Writing Task: Identify Supporting Details Consider what you have learned about the three figures from whose perspective you will write. Consider what you have learned and read in this topic and list three details about each figure to support the main ideas.

Figure 1:	Figure 2:	Figure 3:
Details:	Details:	Details:

Lesson 5 Writing Task: Draw Conclusions Review the details you have collected to draw a conclusion about each medieval figure from whose perspective you will write: What was life like for this person? What role did this person play in society? Why did this person matter? Record your conclusions in the space below.

Writing Task Use the main ideas, details, and conclusions you wrote to write a diary entry for each of the three medieval figures you chose. Be sure to use a distinct voice for each diary entry. Each diary entry should reflect the experiences of these figures in their daily lives, their roles in medieval society, and their interests, hopes, and concerns.

Struggle in Medieval Europe Preview

Essential Question What forces can cause a society to change?

Before you begin this topic, think about the Essential Question by answering the following questions.

1. List three things that might happen that can disrupt the way a family or community functions.

2. Preview the topic by skimming lesson titles, headings, and graphics. Then, place a check mark next to the events that you think may have caused struggle in the Middle Ages.

__war __religion __music and art

__famine __rulers' claims to thrones __floods

__different opinions __peace __plague

Timeline Skills

As you read, write and/or draw at least three events from the topic. Draw a line from each event to its correct position on the timeline.

900	1000	1100

Map Skills

Using maps throughout the topic, label the outline map with the places listed. Then, color England, Iberian Peninsula, and the area of Holy Roman Empire one color, and the Mediterranean Sea a different color.

Iberian Peninsula	Balkan Peninsula	North European Plain
The Alps	England	Italian Peninsula
Mediterranean Sea	Black Sea	North Sea
France	Holy Roman Empire	

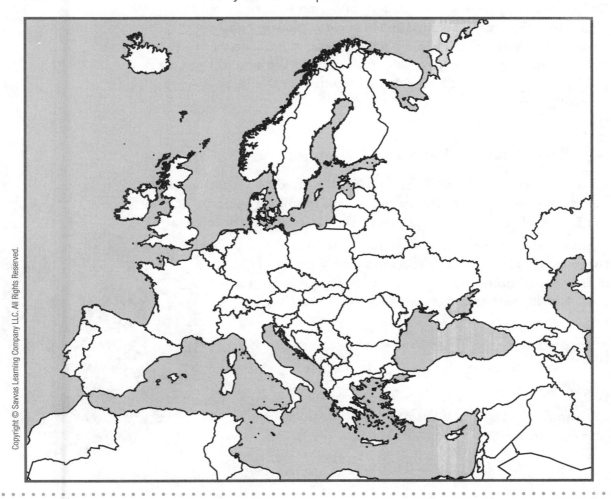

1200	1300	1400	1500

Project-Based Learning Inquiry

Medieval Monarchs Face Conflicts

On this Quest, you will need to find out what events marked significant changes in late Medieval society. You will gather information about the Middle Ages by examining sources in your text and by conducting your own research. At the end of the Quest, you will design a comic book about a conflict in the Middle Ages involving a king or emperor.

① Ask Questions (See Student Text, page 106)

As you begin your Quest, keep in mind the Guiding Question: **What events marked significant changes in late medieval society?** and the Essential Question: **What forces can cause a society to change?**

What other questions do you need to ask in order to answer these questions? Consider the following aspects of life during the Middle Ages. Two questions are filled in for you. Add at least two questions for each category.

Theme Government and the People

Sample questions:

How did the signing of the Magna Carta change the relationship between kings and subjects in England?

What causes contributed to the end of feudalism?

Theme Religion and the Church

Theme Trade and Warfare

Theme Science and Medicine

Theme My Additional Questions

 INTERACTIVE

For extra help with Step 1, review the
21st Century Tutorial: **Ask Questions**.

2 Investigate

As you read about Europe in the Middle Ages, collect five connections from your text to help you answer the Guiding Question. Three are already chosen for you.

Connect to the Magna Carta

Primary Source The Magna Carta (See Student Text, page 121)

Here's a connection! What does this Primary Source tell you about the Magna Carta? What is the significance of the Magna Carta?

How might different kings or emperors of the Middle Ages have felt about the Magna Carta?

Connect to the Crusades

Lesson 3 What Were the Effects of the Crusades? (See Student Text, page 128)

Here's another connection! Examine the effects of the Crusades on the crusaders. How will this change the medieval society of Europe?

How do you think the effects of the Crusades influenced the decisions of rulers?

Connect to the Black Death

Primary Source Giovanni Boccaccio, *The Decameron* (See Student Text, page 146)

What does this connection tell you about the kind of social changes the plague caused in medieval society? Why do you think the plague caused these changes?

How do you think the plague affected the rule of kings and emperors?

It's Your Turn! **Find two more connections. Fill in the title of your connections, then answer the questions. Connections may be images, primary sources, maps, or text.**

Your Choice | Connect to

Location in text

What is the main idea of this connection?

What does it tell you about a conflict involving a king or emperor during the Middle Ages?

Your Choice | Connect to

Location in text

What is the main idea of this connection?

What does it tell you about a conflict involving a king or emperor during the Middle Ages?

Struggle in Medieval Europe

③ Conduct Research (See Student Text, page 148)

Begin your research by finding additional primary and secondary sources of valid information on your own. Fill in the chart to show how these sources provide further information about conflicts involving kings and emperors during the Middle Ages. Use your research to help your team select a specific topic for your comic.

Source	Information About Conflicts

INTERACTIVE

For extra help, review the 21st Century Tutorials: **Work in Teams, Search for Information on the Internet,** and **Avoid Plagiarism.**

 **FINDINGS**

4 Create Your Comic Book (See Student Text, page 148)

You will now work together as a team to fully research, write, illustrate and summarize a comic book about a specific conflict covered in this topic.

1. **Prepare to Write** Decide, as a group, what conflict you would like to focus on and what the title of your comic book will be. Record your decisions below.

Title of Comic Book:

Conflict:

Team Member Assignments

Use the chart below to help your team assign responsibility for each part of your project. You may have more than one teammate working on a given section, or one team member may need to be responsible for more than one section.

Responsibility	Teammate(s) Responsible
Additional Research	
Write Cover	
Illustrate Cover	
Write Illustrated Page	
Draw Illustrated Page	
Write Summary	

2. **Write a Draft** Using your research, outline the pieces of the project according to your responsibilities. Make sure that all of your facts are correct and consistent with your sources.

3. **Share with Your Team** Share your draft with your team. Tell your team what you like about their pieces and suggest any improvements. Use positive and professional language as you critique each others' work.

4. **Finalize Your Project** Correct any grammatical, spelling, or factual errors. Be sure to complete an illustrated cover page, an illustrated page, and a well-written summary of your comic.

5. **Reflect** Think about your experience in completing this topic's Quest. What did you learn about Europe in the Middle Ages and the conflicts involving its rulers? What questions do you still have? How will you answer them?

Reflections

Take Notes

Literacy Skill: Compare and Contrast Use what you have read to complete the diagram. Identify the objectives of the German emperors and the popes. What was different? What was the same?

German Emperors　　　Both　　　Popes

INTERACTIVE

For extra help, review the 21st Century Tutorials: **Compare and Contrast**.

Practice Vocabulary

Word Map Study the word map for the word *excommunicate*. Characteristics are words or phrases that relate to the word in the center of the word map. Non-characteristics are words or phrases not associated with the word. Use the blank word map to explore the meaning of the word *secular*.

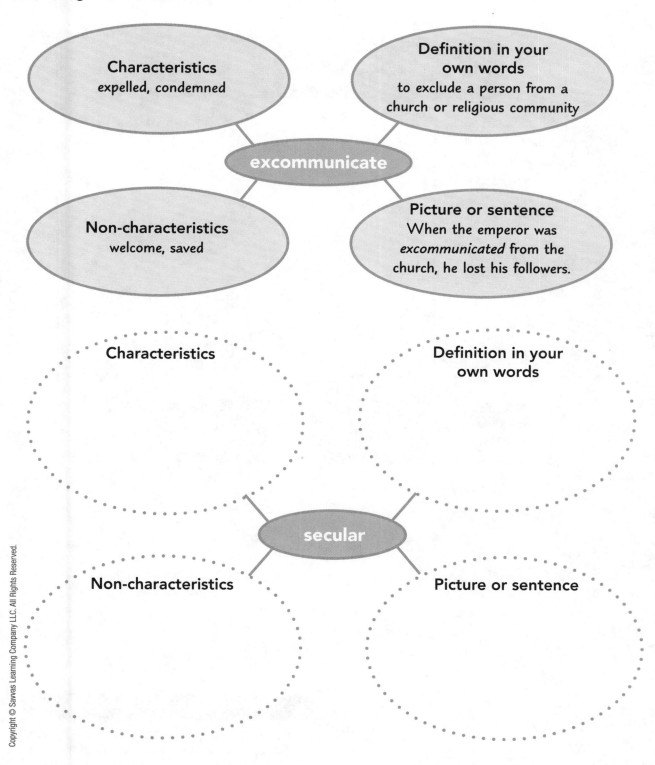

Characteristics
expelled, condemned

Definition in your own words
to exclude a person from a church or religious community

excommunicate

Non-characteristics
welcome, saved

Picture or sentence
When the emperor was *excommunicated* from the church, he lost his followers.

Characteristics

Definition in your own words

secular

Non-characteristics

Picture or sentence

Take Notes

Literacy Skills: Cite Evidence For each statement, cite evidence from the text that supports the idea. One example has been provided for you. Complete the chart with supporting evidence. For the second chart, draw your own conclusion from the text and use evidence to support your claim.

The Magna Carta was one of the most important documents of all time.

The Magna Carta stated that even a king must abide by the law.

The Norman Conquest transformed English history and culture.

INTERACTIVE

For extra help, review the 21st Century Tutorials: **Support Ideas With Evidence**.

Practice Vocabulary

Words in Context For each question below, write an answer that shows your understanding of the boldfaced key term.

1. Why is a **pilgrimage** significant for religious people?

2. What is the significance of the **Magna Carta**?

3. What is **common law**?

4. What is **habeas corpus**, and what is its significance?

5. What is another way of saying a **writ**?

6. What is a **parliament** and why is it important?

7. How was the **judiciary** system first formed in England?

Take Notes

Literacy Skills: Sequence Use what you have read to complete the table. Use the flowchart to sequence the events of the Crusades. In each box, draw or write about important details associated with the event. The first one has been partially filled in for you.

Before the Crusades

• Peter the Hermit rallied thousands of people to join his fight to free Jerusalem.

First Crusade

Second and Third Crusades

Fourth Crusade

Final Crusades

Inquisition

INTERACTIVE

For extra help, review the 21st Century Tutorials: **Sequence**.

Practice Vocabulary

Matching Logic Using your knowledge of the underlined vocabulary words, draw a line from each sentence in Column 1 to match it with the sentence in Column 2 to which it logically belongs.

Column 1	Column 2
1. A lot of people were killed or tortured during the <u>Inquisition</u>.	They were a series of campaigns to establish Christian control in the Holy Land.
2. Many people were excommunicated, exiled, or killed for <u>heresy</u>.	These courts targeted people who did not agree with the church.
3. The <u>Crusades</u> involved peasants, soldiers and kings from across Europe.	The Church did not tolerate differences in religious beliefs.

Quick Activity Crusade Diary

Imagine that you are living at the time of the Crusades. Choose a point of view, and write a short diary entry from that perspective. Consider including details such as: What do you see? How does it make you feel? Why did this crusade take place? Why did people join this crusade? What happened during this crusade? What were some of the results of this crusade? Here are some possible points of view you could choose.

• You are a knight who has joined the First Crusade.

• You are a member of one of the later crusades.

• You live in Constantinople when the Fourth Crusade comes through your city.

Take Notes

Literacy Skills: Summarize Use what you have read to complete the table. Write two details for each main idea, and use them to write a summary of the chapter below. One detail has been provided for you.

Spain Under the Moors	The Reconquista	Spain After the Reconquista
• There was a blend of cultures.	•	•
•	•	•

Summary

INTERACTIVE

For extra help, review the 21st Century Tutorials: **Summarize**.

Practice Vocabulary

True or False? Decide whether each statement below is true or false. Circle T or F, and then explain your answer. Be sure to include the underlined vocabulary word in your explanation. The first one has been completed for you.

1. **T / F** The <u>Iberian Peninsula</u> contains present-day Italy.

   False. The <u>Iberian Peninsula</u> contains present-day Spain and Portugal.

2. **T / F** The <u>Moors</u> ruled a diverse society that made advances in art and medicine.

3. **T / F** The <u>Reconquista</u> was the Christian reclaiming of the Holy Land.

Take Notes

Literacy Skills: Identify Cause and Effect Use what you have read to complete the table. For each event, identify three causes that led to the event. One example has been completed for you.

Effect: The population of Europe decreased dramatically in the 1300s.

Cause:
Famine—bad weather ruined crops and killed livestock, leading to a food shortage

Cause:

Cause:

Effect: The end of the Middle Ages brought the end of feudalism.

Cause:

Cause:

Cause:

INTERACTIVE

For extra help, review the 21st Century Tutorials: **Analyze Cause and Effect**.

Practice Vocabulary

Use a Word Bank Choose one word from the following word bank to fill in each blank. When you have finished, you will have a short summary of important ideas from this section.

Word Bank

bubonic plague   Peasants' Revolt   famine

Black Death   Hundred Years' War

In the 1300s, a series of events caused the decline of medieval society.

Heavy rainfall over two years ruined many crops, leading to widespread

.... across northern Europe. Following

that, a new kind of war, a war between nations, broke out between

England and France. Lasting from 1337–1453, it became known as

the .... After about ten years of war,

the .... spread throughout Asia and

Europe. The population decreased so much that the epidemic became

known as the .... As economic and social

tensions about feudalism increased, English peasants mounted the

.... The end of the Middle Ages was the

beginning of the modern era in Europe.

Quick Activity Dark Times Skit

With a partner or small group, develop a short skit about one of the terrible disasters of the late Middle Ages.

Setting	Character	Plot
Where does your skit take place?	Create at least two characters and describe their names, ages, occupations, and history.	What is the conflict? What events unfold?

Team Challenge First, choose the disaster that your team will focus on. Next, brainstorm its effects on the lives, feelings, and outlook of ordinary people. Use the chart above to outline your skit. Then, write your script on a separate piece of paper.

Which disaster will your skit cover?

____ Famine ____ Plague ____ Hundred Years' War

Writing Workshop: Write a Research Paper

Do research and write a brief account of some aspect of Jewish life in medieval Europe, such as the impact of the Crusades or the Plague on Jewish populations, Jewish life in Spain before or after the Reconquista, or Jewish migration. The prompts below will help guide you through the process.

Lesson 1 Writing Task: Generate Questions to Focus Your Research
(See Student Text, page 112)

What do you know about Jewish life in Medieval Europe? Consider ideas, such as the impact of the Crusades or the Plague on Jewish populations, Jewish life in Spain before or after the Reconquista, or Jewish migration during the Middle Ages. Use the box below to formulate two to four questions and then select one question on which to focus.

Lesson 2 Writing Task: Find and Use Credible Sources
(See Student Text, page 120)

Look for reliable sources that provide credible and accurate information about Jewish life in Medieval Europe. Take notes on information that you may use in your paper. Record web addresses and other source information so you can find them again, and so you can cite accurately.

Source (Title and Author or Web Address)	Notes

Lesson 3 Writing Task: Support Ideas with Evidence
(See Student Text, page 129)

Examine your credible sources for evidence that supports what you have learned about Jewish life in Medieval Europe. Use a separate piece of paper to write a brief outline of your ideas, with supporting details from the text. Be sure to indicate from which source you got your information.

Lesson 4 Writing Task: Cite Sources (See Student Text, page 139)

Review the sources that you noted. Write full citations for all of your sources, following the format provided by your teacher. Include the name of the article or text, the author, the publisher, the date of publication, and the web address (if applicable). This information should be included at the end of your research paper.

Source (Title and Author or Web Address)	Correct Citation

Lesson 5 Writing Task: Use Technology to Produce and Publish
(See Student Text, page 145)

Using your outline and the information you have gathered, write a brief account of some aspect of Jewish life in medieval Europe. Make use of appropriate technology to create and distribute your research paper. Consider your audience as you decide in what form(s) to publish your work.

TOPIC 4

The Islamic World and South Asia Preview

Essential Question How do ideas grow and spread?

Before you begin this topic, think about the Essential Question by completing the following activity.

1. What people, places, experiences, or things have influenced or changed your personal values and ideas?

2. Preview the topic by skimming lesson titles, headlines, and graphics. Then place a check mark next to the items below that you predict will influence how ideas grow and spread.

__traveling   __conquering other lands   __staying home by yourself

__technological advances   __art, architecture, literature __making carpets

__being curious   __talking with people

Timeline Skills

As you read, write and/or draw at least three events from the topic. Draw a line from each event to its correct position on the timeline.

500	700	900

Map Skills

Using maps throughout the topic, label the outline map with the places listed. Then, color the land showing the extent of the Muslim world in the year 1000.

Sasanian Persian empire   Arabia   Europe   Morocco

Egypt   Spain   Asia   Mecca

Medina   Cairo   Baghdad   Jerusalem

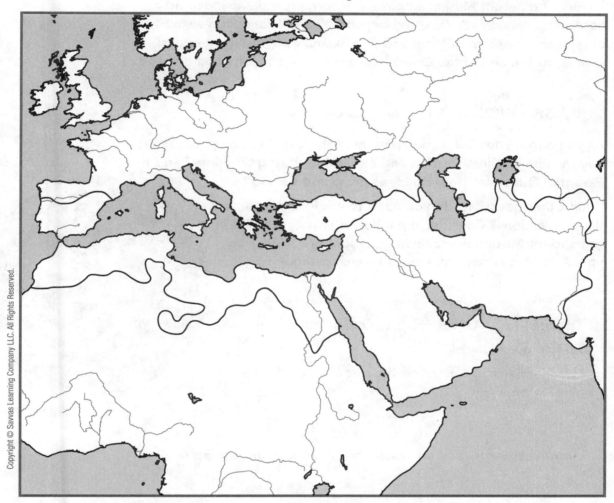

| 1100 | 1300 | 1500 | 1700 |

Quest

Project -Based Learning Inquiry

Growth of Muslim Empires

On this Quest, you need to find out which key events best show the history of different Muslim empires that formed and expanded across Southwest Asia, South Asia, and beyond. You will conduct research about the expansion of Islam and find examples of the most critical events. At the end of the Quest, you will create an illustrated timeline.

1 Ask Questions (See Student Text, page 154)

As you begin your Quest, keep in mind the Guiding Question: **What key Muslim empires formed and expanded during this time?** and the Essential Question: **How do ideas grow and spread?**

What other questions do you need to ask in order to answer these questions? Consider the following aspects of life in the ancient Muslim world. Two questions are filled in for you. Add at least two questions in each category.

Theme Art, Architecture, and Literature

Sample questions:

How does architecture reveal the spread and influence of Muslim empires?

How did literature and art reflect the spread of Islam and other ideas?

Theme Trade

Theme Warfare and Conquest

Theme Religion and Cultural Life

Theme Science, Mathematics, and Medicine

Theme My Additional Questions

 INTERACTIVE

For help with Step 1, review the
21st Century Skills Tutorial: **Ask Questions**.

Quest CONNECTIONS

② Investigate

As you read about the growth and expansion of Muslim empires, collect five connections from your text to help you answer the Guiding Question. Three connections are already chosen for you.

Connect to the Spread of Islam

Lesson 3 The Caliphs (See Student Text, page 168)

Here's a connection! Examine the how cultures change. What cultural changes did the spread of Islam during the time of the caliphs bring within empires? How did these changes affect society?

How did those changes affect the expansion of Muslim empires?

Connect to Timelines

Analysis Skills Construct a Timeline (See Student Text, page 173)

Here's another connection! What other events do you think would help show what key Muslim empires formed and expanded? Where do they fall on the timeline?

What changes did they inspire?

Connect to the Arrival of Islam in India

Lesson 6 Islam Arrives in India (See Student Text, page 191)

What does this connection tell you about the specific events that brought Islam to India?

What new ideas came from that meeting of cultures?

It's Your Turn! **Find two more connections. Fill in the title of your connections, then answer the questions. Connections may be images, primary sources, maps, or text.**

Your Choice | Connect to

Location

What is the main idea of this connection?

What does it tell you about how ideas grow and spread?

Your Choice | Connect to

What is the main idea of this connection?

What does it tell you about how ideas grow and spread?

③ Conduct Research (See Student Text, page 194)

Begin your research by finding out more about the various empires and dynasties of the Islamic world from the 600s to the 1600s. Fill in the chart below with key events and dates to help you organize your information. Circle the dates since they will become the key to designing and organizing your timeline.

Empire or Dynasty	Important Events and Dates

👆 INTERACTIVE

For extra help with Step 3, review the 21st Century Skills Tutorial: **Sequence**.

4 Make Your illustrated Timeline (See Student Text, page 194)

Now it's time to put together all of the information you have gathered and use it to create your illustrated timeline.

1. **Prepare to Write** Begin by looking through your information above and choosing the events that you think are most important to the expansion of key empires in the Muslim world. Then use the flowchart below to put your events in chronological order.

2. **Write a Draft** Create a rough draft listing the events you want to include on your timeline. Decide on the start and end dates and how long the time intervals will be. Include notes on the design. For example, you might want to include color-coded bars showing the length of time for each empire and how they overlapped. Choose or draw illustrations to go with your events.

3. **Share with a Partner** Exchange your draft with a partner. Tell your partner what you like about his or her draft and suggest any improvements.

4. **Finalize Your Timeline** Correct any spelling or grammatical errors. Use technology to finalize and publish your timeline.

5. **Reflect on the Quest** Think about your experience completing this topic's Quest. What did you learn about Muslim empires and how they expanded? What questions do you still have about the Muslim empires? How will you answer them?

Reflections

Take Notes

Literacy Skills: Identify Main Ideas and Details Use what you have read to complete the table. In each space, write one main idea and two details. The first column is completed for you.

The Arabian Setting	The Rise of Islam
Main Idea: The environment significantly influenced life in Arabia. **Details:** The harsh environment helped keep foreign invaders out. In dry regions, people depend on oases for water, because there is very little water otherwise.	**Main Idea:** **Details:**

Preaching a New Message	The Hijra
Main Idea: **Details:**	**Main Idea:** **Details:**

INTERACTIVE

For extra help, review the 21st Century Skills Tutorial: **Identify Main Ideas and Detail**.

Practice Vocabulary

True or False? Decide whether each statement below is true or false. Circle T or F, and then explain your answer. Be sure to include the underlined vocabulary word in your explanation. The first one is done for you.

1. **T / F** An <u>oasis</u> is a place in the desert where only sand can be found.
   False; An <u>oasis</u> is a place in the desert where water can be found.

2. **T / F** Muhammad said that <u>revelations</u> he received in the cave were messages from God.

3. **T / F** <u>Nomads</u> are people who live in one place for their entire lives.

4. **T / F** The <u>Hijra</u> is another name for Muhammad's journey back to Mecca.

5. **T / F** A <u>prophet</u> is a person believed to bring messages to the people from God.

Quick Activity **Caption This!**

With a partner, analyze the following three images.

Team Challenge! With your partner, write a short caption for each image that explains how geography affects an aspect of life in Arabia. Post your captions to the class board.

Take Notes

Literacy Skills: Summarize Use what you have read to complete the chart. Then write a summary of the section in the box below.

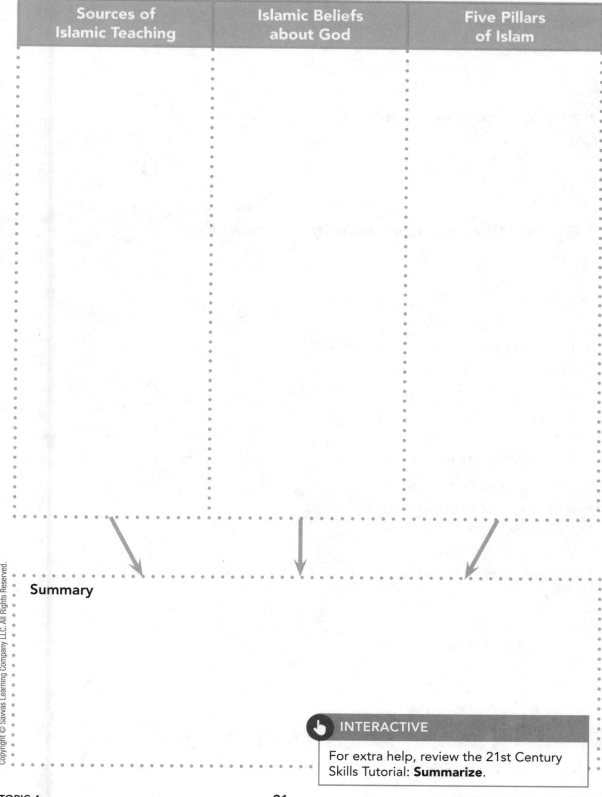

Sources of Islamic Teaching	Islamic Beliefs about God	Five Pillars of Islam

Summary

> 👆 INTERACTIVE
>
> For extra help, review the 21st Century Skills Tutorial: **Summarize**.

Practice Vocabulary

Sentence Builder Finish the sentences below with a key term from this section. You may have to change the form of the words to complete the sentences.

Word Bank

Quran	Sunnah	hajj
mosque	Sharia	

1. A Muslim house of worship is called a

2. Guidelines for living a proper Muslim life are provided by the

3. The Islamic code of law is known as the

4. The pilgrimage to Mecca is called the

5. The holy book of Islam is called the

Lesson 3 Expansion of the Muslim World

Take Notes

Literacy Skills: Sequence Use what you have read to complete the timeline. Sequence the events that marked the expansion of the Muslim world. For each date, write or draw in the box about a significant event that occurred at that time. The first one is completed for you.

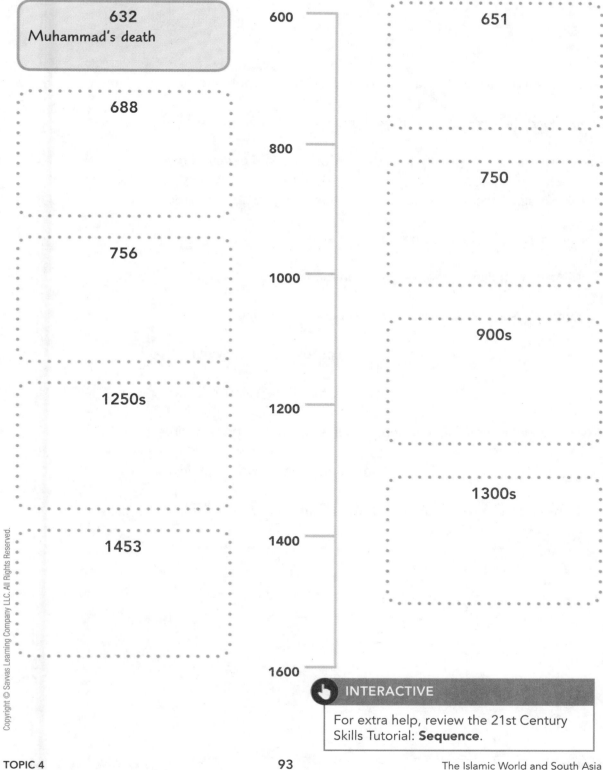

632
Muhammad's death

688

756

1250s

1453

600

800

1000

1200

1400

1600

651

750

900s

1300s

INTERACTIVE

For extra help, review the 21st Century Skills Tutorial: **Sequence**.

Practice Vocabulary

Use a Word Bank Choose one word from the word bank to fill in each blank. When you have finished, you will have a short summary of important ideas from the section.

Word Bank

Sufism   Shia   dynasty

sultans   caliph   Sunni

After Muhammad's death, his followers disagreed about who

should lead their community. It lead to a split between the two

sects: .... Muslims, who believed that

the community needed a leader with political skills and supported

Muhammad's main advisor, and the ....

Muslims, who believed that only Muhammad's relatives should

become the leader. When Muhammad's cousin became the

fourth ...., or ruler, the Umayyad

.... was established. As Islam spread and

expanded, an Islamic lifestyle that stresses controlling ones desires, called

........................., emerged. After the Mongol invasions,

non-Arab rulers in some surviving Muslim states called themselves

....

Take Notes

Literacy Skills: Identify Cause and Effect Use what you have read to complete the table. Write the effects of each event or idea below. The first one is completed for you.

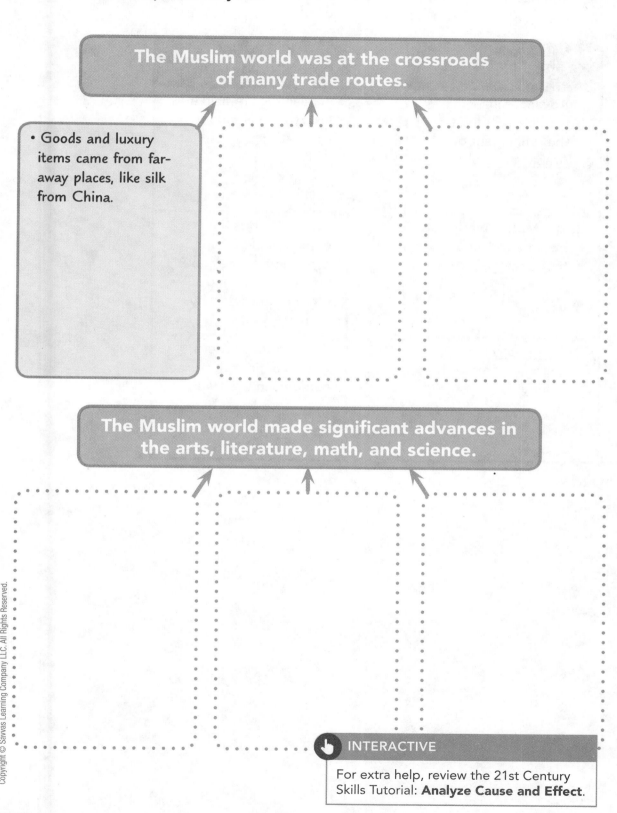

The Muslim world was at the crossroads of many trade routes.

- Goods and luxury items came from far-away places, like silk from China.

The Muslim world made significant advances in the arts, literature, math, and science.

INTERACTIVE

For extra help, review the 21st Century Skills Tutorial: **Analyze Cause and Effect**.

Practice Vocabulary

Matching Logic Using your knowledge of the underlined vocabulary words, draw a line from each sentence in Column 1 to match it with the sentence in Column 2 to which it logically belongs.

Column 1	Column 2
1. Advances in mathematics led to the refinement of <u>Arabic numerals</u>.	Persian rugs remain a luxury item in modern times.
2. The Muslim world became well known for its <u>textile</u> work.	Islam prohibits the depiction of humans and animals in religious art, so Muhammad is often represented by his name.
3. <u>Calligraphy</u> is a merging of art and writing.	Much of the modern world continues to write numbers in this style.

Quick Activity

Fun with Words! Many words in the English language originally come from another language. Some common English words are derived from Arabic. Examine the Arabic words below.

Arabic Word	English Definition	English Word
Sukkar	a natural fiber that many clothing products are made from	
Qutn	a caffeinated beverage that many people drink in the morning	
Al-jabr	a comfortable piece of furniture	
Qahwa	a method of mathematics useful for solving problems	
Suffa	a sweetener	

Team Challenge! Working with a partner, draw a line from each Arabic word to its English definition. Then write the modern English word that derives from the Arabic word in the box next to its definition.

Take Notes

Literacy Skills: Summarize Use what you have read to complete the
table. Fill in notes about important aspects of life under the Gupta
empire. Then, use your notes to write a summary of this lesson.

Government	Culture	Achievements

Summary:

 INTERACTIVE

For extra help, review the 21st Century
Skills Tutorial: **Summarize**.

Practice Vocabulary

Word Map Study the word map for the word *citizenship*. Characteristics are words or phrases that relate to the word in the center of the word map. Non-characteristics are words and phrases not associated with the word. Use the blank word map to explore the meaning of the word *numeral*. Then make word maps of your own for these words: *decimal system* and *metallurgy*.

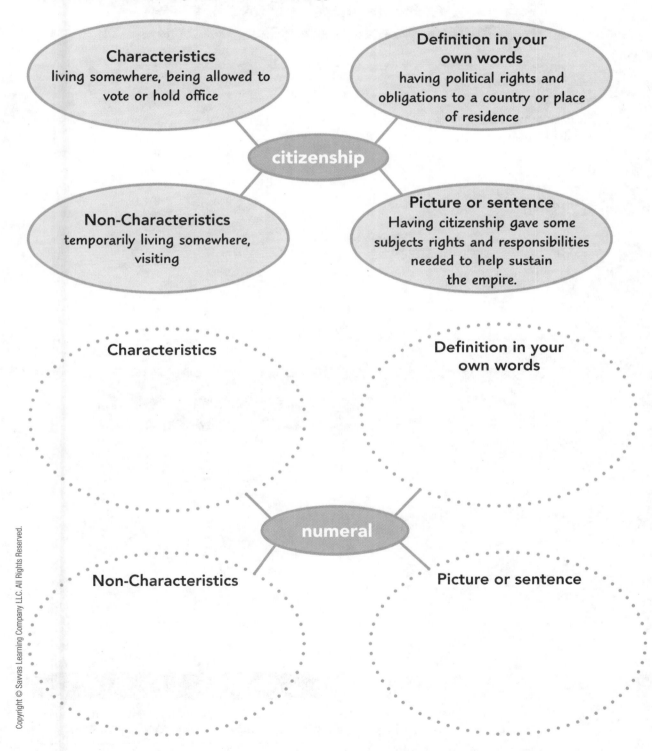

Characteristics
living somewhere, being allowed to vote or hold office

Definition in your own words
having political rights and obligations to a country or place of residence

citizenship

Non-Characteristics
temporarily living somewhere, visiting

Picture or sentence
Having citizenship gave some subjects rights and responsibilities needed to help sustain the empire.

Characteristics

Definition in your own words

numeral

Non-Characteristics

Picture or sentence

Take Notes

Literacy Skills: Cite Evidence Use what you have read to complete the table. Cite three pieces of evidence from the text that support each main idea below. The first one has been completed for you.

> **Trade and expansion affected the development of Hinduism and Buddhism.**

Maritime and overland trade allowed people to exchange ideas with members of other faiths.

> **The arrival of Islam changed the political, cultural, and religious landscape in much of India.**

INTERACTIVE

For extra help, review the 21st Century Skills Tutorial: **Support Ideas With Evidence**.

Practice Vocabulary

Word Map Study the word map for the word *maritime*. Characteristics are words or phrases that relate to the word in the center of the word map. Non-characteristics are words and phrases not associated with the word. Use the blank word map to explore the meaning of the word *Bhakti*. Then make your own word map for the word *bodhisattva*.

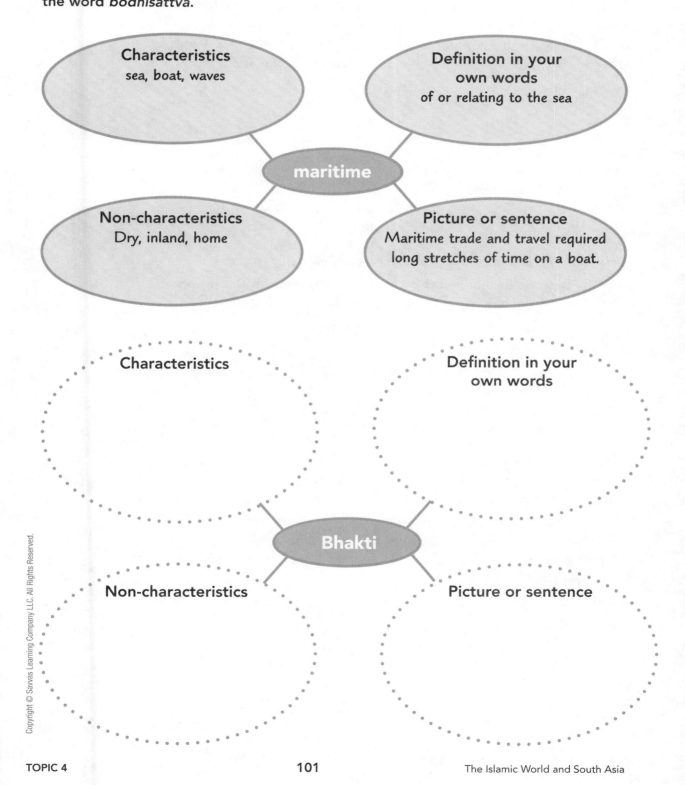

Writing Workshop Arguments

As you read, develop a claim in response to this question: **Was conquest or trade the key factor in the growth of Islamic empires?** The prompts below will help walk you through the process.

Lesson 1 Writing Task: Introduce Claim (See Student Text, page 158)

Write one sentence that states your claim about whether you think conquest or trade was the key factor in the growth of Islamic empires. This will be your thesis statement for the argument that you will write at the end of the topic. You may change your thesis as you learn more.

Lesson 2 Writing Task: Support Claim (See Student Text, page 163)

Identify two details that you think might help explain why Islam spread. These details will help you support your claim for your argument.

Lesson 3 Writing Task: Use Credible Sources (See Student Text, page 172)

Choose one source of information that you will use to research your argument about the expansion of Islam. Write a paragraph that identifies the source and explain why you think the source is credible, or believable.

Lesson 4 Writing Task: Distinguish Claims from Opposing Claims
(See Student Text, page 180)

Imagine arguments for and against your main ideas about whether conquest or trade was a key factor in the growth of Islamic empires.

Your Claims	Opposing Claims

Lesson 5 and 6 Writing Task: Write an Introduction and a Conclusion
(See Student Text, pages 186 and 192)

Revise your thesis sentence and write a draft of an introductory paragraph for your essay, introducing your main ideas. Draft a conclusion paragraph, revisiting the thesis from a different angle and formulating how you will leave a lasting impression.

Writing Task (See Student Text, page 195)

Using all of the components that you have created, write an argument about whether conquest or trade was the key factor in the growth of Islamic empires. As you write, consider using signal words to help you transition between making your claims and addressing counterclaims.

5 Civilizations of East Asia and Southeast Asia Preview

Essential Question How Do Ideas Grow and Spread?

Before you begin this topic, think about the Essential Question by answering the following question.

1. Think about the language that you speak and write, traditions that you celebrate, food that you know how to grow or prepare, beliefs that you have, skills that you possess, and stories and songs that you know. How did you learn about these things? Write your answers below.

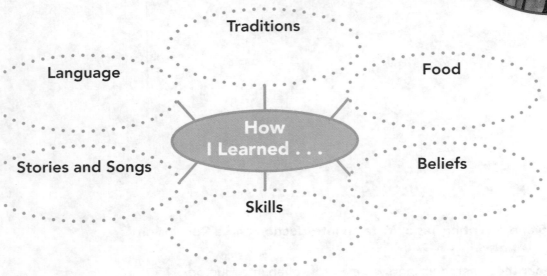

Traditions

Language

Food

How I Learned . . .

Stories and Songs

Beliefs

Skills

Timeline Skills

As you read, write and/or draw at least three events from the topic. Draw a line from each event to its correct position on the timeline.

400	600	800

Map Skills

Using maps throughout the topic, label the outline map with the places listed. Then color in water, desert, plains, plateau, and mountains.

China	Japan	Korean Peninsula
Pacific Ocean	Sea of Japan (East Sea)	Yellow Sea
Huang River	Chang River	Mekong River

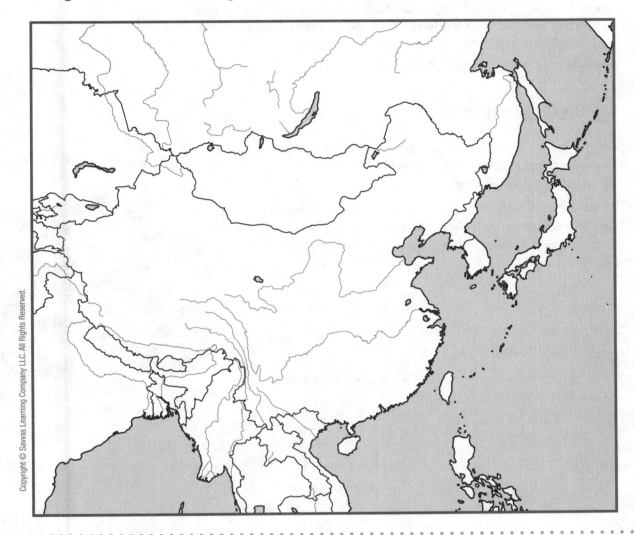

1000

1200

1400

Quest

Document-Based Writing Inquiry

A Strong Influence

On this Quest, you will explore primary and secondary sources about the influence of ancient China on other cultures in East Asia and Southeast Asia. At the end of the Quest you will write an explanatory essay about China's influence.

1 Ask Questions (See Student Text, page 200)

As you begin your Quest, keep in mind the Guiding Question: **How did China influence the cultures around it?** and the Essential Question: **How do ideas grow and spread?**

What other questions do you need to ask in order to answer the Guiding Question? Think about the following aspects of life in East Asia and Southeast Asia. Two questions are filled in for you. Add at least two questions for each category.

Theme Economic Activity

Sample questions:

What economic contact did China have with other cultures in East Asia and Southeast Asia?

What elements of China's economy appeared in neighboring lands?

Theme Government and Society

Theme Technology and Innovation

Theme Religion and Philosophy

Theme Arts and Literature

Theme My Additional Questions

 INTERACTIVE

For extra help with Step 1, review the 21st Century Skills Tutorial: **Ask Questions.**

Quest CONNECTIONS

2 Investigate

As you read about ancient China and other cultures in East Asia and Southeast Asia, collect five connections from your text to help you answer the Guiding Question. Three connections are already chosen for you.

Connect to the Spread of Buddhism

Lesson 3 Chinese Belief Systems (See Student Text, page 228)

Here's a connection! Study the map. Where did Buddhism originate? Where did it spread?

How does this source demonstrate the spread of ideas?

Connect to the Constitution of Seventeen Articles

Lesson 4 How Did Shotoku Strengthen Japan? (See Student Text, page 235)

Here's another connection! Read the quote from the Constitution of Seventeen Articles. How does the quote reflect Chinese influence?

How does this source demonstrate the spread of ideas?

Connect to Chinese and Japanese Architecture

Lesson 6 Japan's Golden Age (See Student Text, page 248)

Study the images of temple structures found in China and Japan. Compare the styles of architecture. How are they similar and different? What purpose do the structures share?

How does this source demonstrate the spread of ideas?

It's your turn! **Find two more connections on your own. Fill in the title of your connections, then answer the questions. Connections may be images, primary sources, maps, or text.**

Your Choice | Connect to

Location in text
What is the main idea of this connection?

What does this source demonstrate about the spread of ideas in East Asia and Southeast Asia?

Your Choice | Connect to

Location in text
What is the main idea of this connection?

What does this source demonstrate about the spread of ideas in East Asia and Southeast Asia?

③ Examine Primary and Secondary Sources (See Student Text, page 260)

Examine the primary and secondary sources provided online or from your teacher. Fill in the chart to show how these sources provide further information about the spread of ideas from China to other parts of East Asia and Southeast Asia. The first one is done for you.

Source	How Source Demonstrates the Spread of Ideas from China
Song for the Peace of the People	Shows the spread of Chinese characters as well as Buddhist and Confucian belief systems to Korea
Van Hanh Zen Temple in Vietnam	
Regional Court Examination in Vietnam	
The Spread of Chinese Civilization to Japan	
Chinese, Korean, and Japanese Writing Systems	

👆 **INTERACTIVE**

For extra help with Step 3, review the 21st Century Skills Tutorials: **Analyze Primary and Secondary Sources** and **Analyze Images.**

Quest FINDINGS

4 Write Your Explanatory Essay (See Student Text, page 260)

Now it's time to put together all of the information you have gathered and use it to write your explanatory essay.

1. **Prepare to Write** You have collected connections and explored documents that show the spread and influence of Chinese culture to neighboring lands and peoples. Look through your notes and decide what evidence of this influence on Korea, Japan, and Southeast Asia you want to discuss in your essay. Summarize your evidence here.

Evidence

2. Write a Thesis Statement Your explanatory essay should answer the Guiding Question: **How did China influence the cultures around it?** Use the information you gathered to write a thesis statement in response to the question.

3. Write a Draft Your essay should build on your thesis statement by providing evidence to explain that China influenced the cultures around it. Review the evidence you recorded. Plan your essay by numbering each piece of evidence in the order you want to present the information in your essay. Then, write a draft of your explanatory essay. Remember to include an introductory paragraph that includes your thesis statement, as well as a concluding paragraph to restate the thesis. The body of your essay should comprise three to five paragraphs that present and explain evidence from the Quest Connections and Quest Source documents.

4. Share with a Partner Exchange drafts with a partner. Read and provide feedback on the drafts. Be sure to consider whether each draft adequately and clearly answers the Guiding Question and provides sufficient evidence to support the thesis statement.

5. Finalize Your Essay Revise your essay. Correct any grammatical or spelling errrors.

6. Reflect on the Quest Think about your experience completing this topic's Quest. What did you learn about the influence of ancient China on neighboring cultures in Korea, Japan, and Southeast Asia? What questions do you still have about these distinct cultures? How will you answer them?

Reflections

 INTERACTIVE

For extra help with Step 4, review the 21st Century Skills Tutorial: **Write an Essay.**

Take Notes

Literacy Skills: Identify Main Ideas and Details Use what you have read to complete the concept web. Record main ideas from the lesson. The first one has been completed for you.

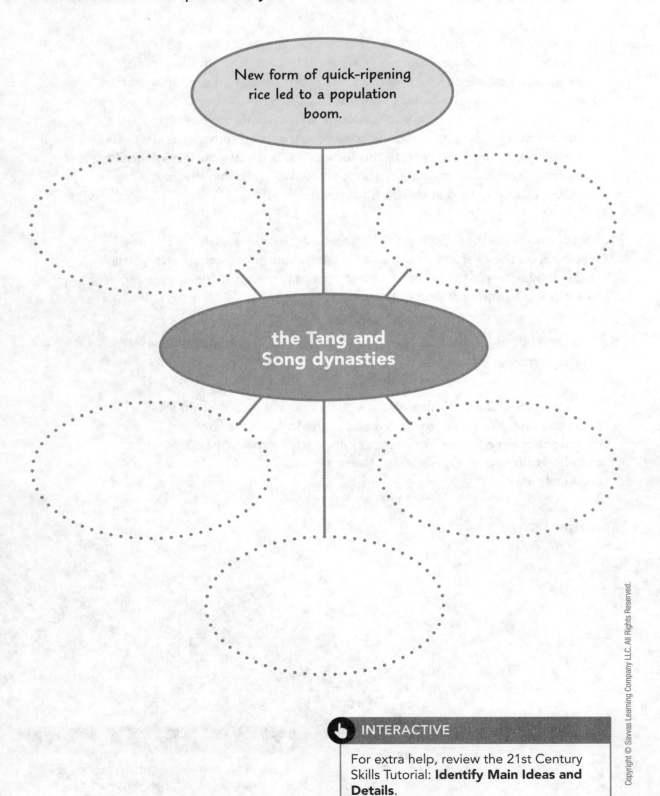

New form of quick-ripening rice led to a population boom.

the Tang and Song dynasties

👆 **INTERACTIVE**

For extra help, review the 21st Century Skills Tutorial: **Identify Main Ideas and Details**.

Practice Vocabulary

Vocabulary Quiz Show Some quiz shows ask a question and expect the contestant to give the answer. In other shows, the contestant is given an answer and must supply the question. If the blank is in the Question column, write the question that would result in the answer in the Answer column. If the question is supplied, write the answer.

Question	Answer
1. What method of promotion rewards skills and talent?	1.
2.	2. porcelain
3. What system of exchange uses currency, rather than bartering?	3.
4.	4. urbanization
5. What were civil servants in China called?	5.
6.	6. bureaucracy

Take Notes

Literacy Skills: Sequence Use what you have read to complete the timeline. Record important events about the Mongol horde, as well as about the Yuan and Ming dynasties in China. The first one has been completed for you.

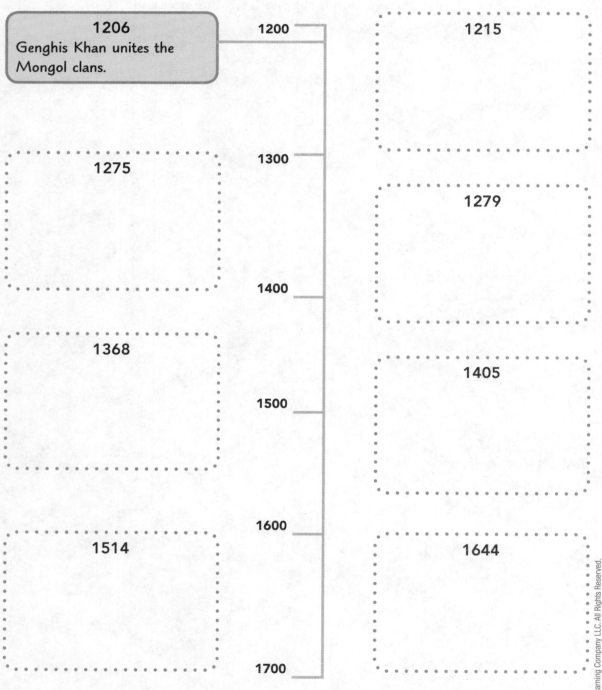

1206
Genghis Khan unites the Mongol clans.

1200

1215

1300

1275

1279

1400

1368

1500

1405

1600

1514

1644

1700

INTERACTIVE

For extra help, review the 21st Century Skills Tutorial: **Sequence**.

Practice Vocabulary

Sentence Builder Finish the sentences below with a vocabulary term from this section. You may have to change the form of the words to complete the sentences.

Word Bank

despot   khan   nomad

smuggler   steppe   tribute

1. The terms *large*, *dry*, and *grass-covered* describe a

```
.........................................
.                                       .
.                                       .
.                                       .
.........................................
```

2. A cruel tyrant or dictator is also called a

```
.........................................
.                                       .
.                                       .
.........................................
```

3. Someone who moves from place to place according to the seasons is called a

```
.........................................
.                                       .
.                                       .
.........................................
```

4. To show their leadership, Genghis and Kublai took the title

```
.........................................
.                                       .
.                                       .
.........................................
```

5. Ming China forced several foreign countries to make payments called

```
.........................................
.                                       .
.                                       .
.........................................
```

6. People who trade illegally are called

```
.........................................
.                                       .
.                                       .
.........................................
```

Take Notes

Literacy Skills: Identify Main Idea and Details Use what you have read
to complete the chart. In each column, write a main idea and then
support it with details from the text.

Technology	Arts	Belief Systems	Influence

INTERACTIVE

For extra help, review the 21st Century Skills
Tutorial: **Identify Main Ideas and Details**.

Practice Vocabulary

For each question below, write an answer that shows your understanding of the boldfaced vocabulary term.

1. What steps does **block printing** involve?

2. What advantage did the **compass** provide?

3. What does **Daoism** teach?

4. What are the basic values of **Confucianism**?

5. Why did **Buddhism** appeal to the Chinese during troubled times?

Quick Activity Ways of Thinking and Believing

Read the primary source excerpts below. Identify each quote as reflecting the beliefs of Buddhism, Confucianism, or Daoism.

They are few who, being filial and fraternal, are fond of offending against their superiors. There have been none, who, not liking to offend against their superiors, have been fond of stirring up confusion. The superior man bends his attention to what is radical. That being established, all practical courses naturally grow up. Filial piety and fraternal submission—are they not the root of all benevolent actions?

NOT exalting worth keeps the people from rivalry. Not prizing what is hard to procure keeps the people from theft. Not to show them what they may covet is the way to keep their minds from disorder. Therefore the Sage, when he governs, empties their minds and fills their bellies, weakens their inclinations and strengthens their bones.... He practises inaction, and nothing remains ungoverned.

Moved by their selfish desires, people seek after fame and glory. But when they have acquired it, they are already stricken in years. If you hanker after worldly fame and practise not the Way, your labors are wrongfully applied and your energy is wasted. It is like unto burning an incense stick. However much its pleasing odor be admired, the fire that consumes is steadily burning up the stick.

Team Challenge! Choose one of the belief systems described in Lesson 3: Buddhism, Daoism, or Confucianism. In the space below, write an explanation of the core beliefs of the belief system you chose. Then, circulate around the class room. With your classmates, take turns sharing your explanation and identifying the belief system.

Take Notes

Literacy Skills: Sequence Use what you have read to complete the timeline. In each space write the event that occurred on that date. The first one has been completed for you.

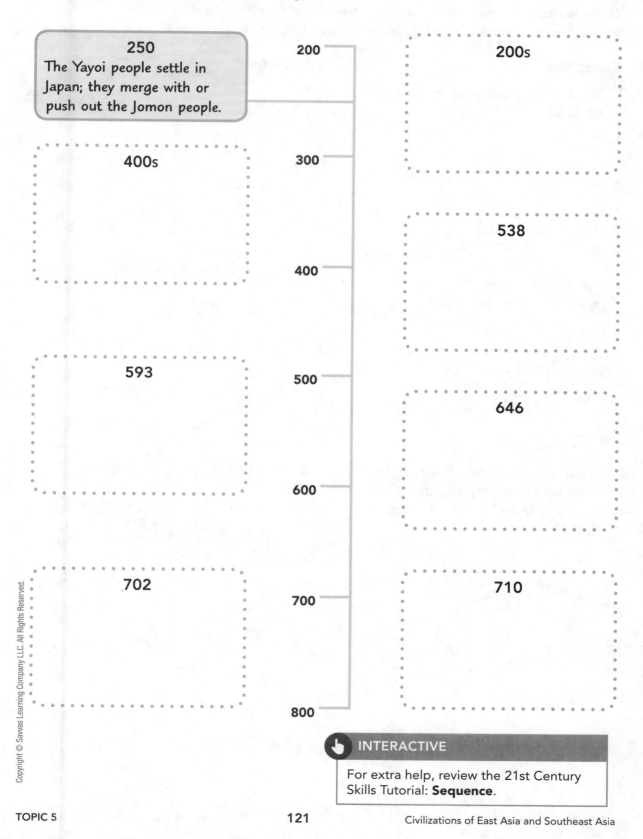

250
The Yayoi people settle in Japan; they merge with or push out the Jomon people.

200

200s

400s

300

538

400

593

500

646

600

702

700

710

800

👆 **INTERACTIVE**

For extra help, review the 21st Century Skills Tutorial: **Sequence**.

Practice Vocabulary

Vocabulary Quiz Show Some quiz shows ask a question and expect the contestant to give the answer. In other shows, the contestant is given an answer and must supply the question. If the blank is in the Question column, write the question that would result in the answer in the Answer column. If the question is supplied, write the answer.

Question	Answer
1. What is an area that forms part of a continent?	1.
2.	2. archipelago
3. What is the name for a group of people with a common ancestor?	3.
4.	4. regent
5. According to ancient Japanese belief, what holy being represents a spirit of nature, a sacred place, an ancestor, or a clan?	5.

Quick Activity Guiding Principles

In 604, Prince Shotoku of Japan authored the Constitution of Seventeen Articles. The Articles provided guidelines to strengthen the central government against the power of competing warlords and clans. Read the excerpts from the Articles below. As you read, underline the part of each article that suggests why that guideline should be followed. Then, explain what the guideline means, in your own words, and explain whether you agree or disagree with the guideline and why.

1. Deal [fairly] with the legal complaints which are submitted to you. If the man who is to decide suits at law makes gain his motive, and hears cases with a view to receiving bribes, then the suits of the rich man will be like a stone flung into water, meeting no resistance, while the complaints of the poor will be like water thrown upon a stone. In these circumstances the poor man will not know where to go, nor will he behave as he should.

2. Know the difference between merit [good behavior] and demerit [bad behavior], and deal out to each its reward and punishment. In these days, reward does not always follow merit, or punishment follow crime. You high officials who have charge of public affairs, make it your business to give clear rewards and punishments.

Team Challenge! Share your explanations and ideas in a small group. Together, on a separate sheet of paper, write three to five guiding principles that your group thinks would make any government better.

Take Notes

Literacy Skills: Analyze Cause and Effect Use what you have read to complete the chart. In the left box, list the causes of feudalism. In the right box, list the effects of feudalism. The first cause has been completed for you.

Causes of Feudalism	Effects of Feudalism
• Widespread violence and lawlessness	•

INTERACTIVE

For extra help, review the 21st Century Skills Tutorial: **Analyze Cause and Effect**.

Practice Vocabulary

Word Bank Choose one word from the word bank to fill in each blank. When you have finished, you will have a short summary of important ideas from the section.

Word Bank

bushido   daimyo   feudalism

figurehead   samurai   shogun

A series of emperors ruled Japan. They gave nobles powerful positions within their courts. One family, the Fujiwara, gained more and more power. Eventually, the Fujiwara became more powerful than the emperor. Although he remained on the throne, the emperor became a .... who ruled in name only.

Other clans arose and fought for power. A member of the Minamoto clan gained the title of ...., or supreme military commander. He became so powerful that he ruled Japan. Nevertheless, lawlessness and violence were widespread. This led to the development of a new social system. Based on social, economic, and political relationships, this system was called .... Land-owning lords became responsible for protecting the people. In return for their protection, the .... received labor from the peasants. Warriors called .... also served the lords. These warriors followed the code of .... Each warrior took great care with his personal appearance and practiced extreme loyalty to his lord.

Take Notes

Literacy Skills: Identify Main Idea and Details Use what you have read to complete the chart. In each space write one main idea and two details.

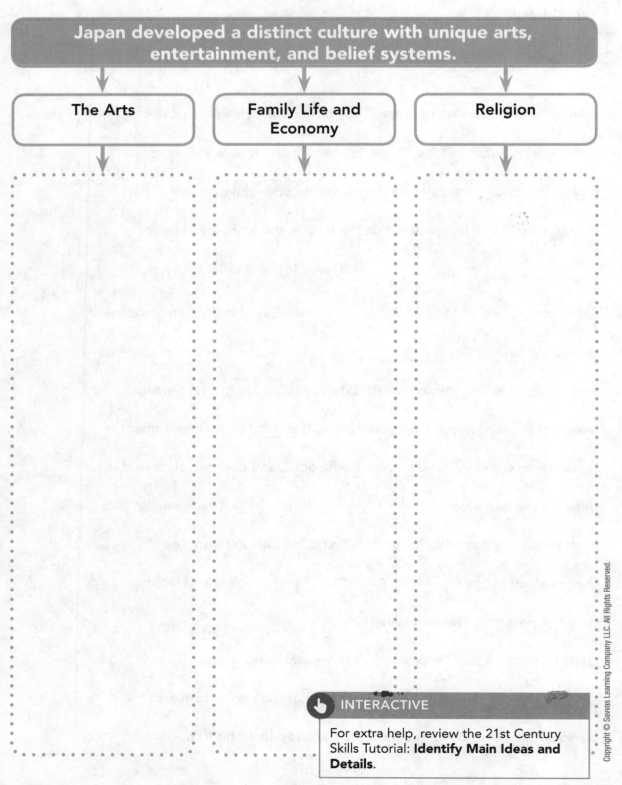

Japan developed a distinct culture with unique arts, entertainment, and belief systems.

The Arts	Family Life and Economy	Religion

INTERACTIVE

For extra help, review the 21st Century Skills Tutorial: **Identify Main Ideas and Details**.

Practice Vocabulary

Words in Context For each question below, write an answer that shows your understanding of the boldfaced vocabulary term.

1. Which classes in Japanese society were most likely to enjoy **Noh**?

2. What groups of people did **Kabuki** aim to entertain?

3. Why did Confucianism encourage people to seek **consensus**?

4. How is **Shinto** different from most other religions?

5. Where do the Japanese build **shrines**?

6. How does one use a **mantra**?

Take Notes

Literacy Skills: Analyze Text Structure Use what you have read to complete the charts. As you move through the lesson, record key details about the subjects listed. The first one has been completed for you.

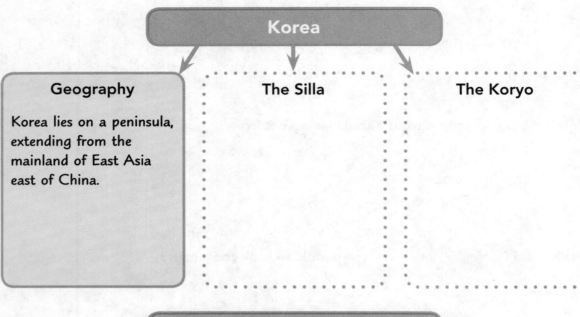

Korea

Geography

Korea lies on a peninsula, extending from the mainland of East Asia east of China.

The Silla

The Koryo

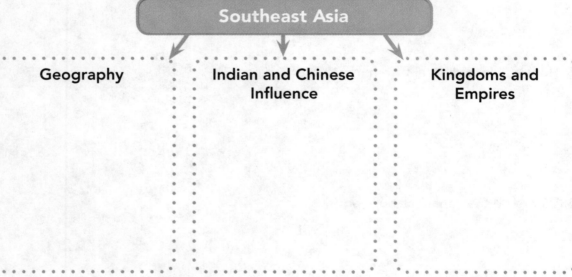

Southeast Asia

Geography

Indian and Chinese Influence

Kingdoms and Empires

Explain how the headings in the lesson organize the text both thematically (by region) and chronologically.

 INTERACTIVE

For extra help, review the 21st Century Skills Tutorial: **Summarize**.

Practice Vocabulary

True or False? Decide whether each statement below is true or false. Circle T or F, and then explain your answer. Be sure to include the underlined vocabulary word in your explanation.

---

1. T / F The development of <u>Hangul</u> helped the spread of Buddhism in Korea.

True; At first, Koreans used Chinese characters to print Buddhist texts, but in time, they developed their own writing system, known as <u>Hangul</u>.

---

2. T / F Koreans learned to make <u>celadon</u> from the Chinese.

3. T / F Southeast Asia includes several <u>archipelagos</u>, including those of Indonesia and the Philippines.

4. T / F Merchant ships tended to dock in port cities in Southeast Asia during <u>monsoons</u>.

5. T / F The construction of <u>stupas</u> demonstrated the strong influence of Japan on Southeast Asia.

Writing Workshop Research Paper

As you read, build a response to this question: **How did new technology and innovations affect China, Japan, Korea, and Southeast Asia?** The prompts below will help walk you through the process.

Lesson 1 Writing Task: Generate Questions to Focus Research
(See Student Text, page 208)

List questions that you have about technologies and innovations in this region. You will use these questions to guide your research and writing.

Lessons 2 and 3 Writing Task: Support Ideas With Evidence and Develop a Clear Thesis (See Student Text, pages 219 and 230)

Your research paper will address the effects of technology and innovation in East and Southeast Asia during the medieval time period. Begin to write the first part of your thesis by answering the following question: What affect did technology have on China? Collect evidence from the first three lessons to support your response. As you move through the rest of the lessons, revise your response to include Japan, Korea, and Southeast Asia.

Lesson 4 Writing Task: Find and Use Credible Sources
(See Student Text, page 237)

You will need to conduct independent research to complete this paper. To find answers to your questions about technology and innovation in this region, you will need to find historical sources in the library, on the Internet, and in academic periodicals. Online, you should search for information on specific topics, such as technology and farming in Yamato, Japan. Look for sources on websites ending in .edu and .gov. These tend to be more reliable. Avoid using blogs, discussion boards, and other social media sources. Below, list one print source and one digital source that you will use. On a separate sheet of paper, write complete source citations for your sources according to the directions given by your teacher.

Lesson 5 Writing Task: Cite Sources (See Student Text, page 244)

Begin taking notes from additional sources on the impact of Chinese and Japanese technology and innovation. You should record your notes on note cards that you can easily organize according to topic and source. As you take notes, be sure to keep track of your sources.

Lesson 6 Writing Task: Organize Your Essay (See Student Text, page 252)

Revise the thesis statement that you began to write in Lesson 3 as needed. Then, review your notes. Decide how you will organize your essay. For example, you may wish to organize your essay according to country, according to types of technologies and innovations, or chronologically. Plan your paper by completing an outline on a separate sheet of paper.

Lesson 7 Writing Task: Draft Your Essay (See Student Text, page 259)

You are ready to begin writing! Use your thesis, your notes, and your outline to write a draft of your research paper. Remember to include appropriate citations for the information that you include. When you have finished, exchange drafts with a partner and provide feedback. Revise your draft based on your partner's feedback.

Writing Task (See Student Text, page 261)

Be sure that your revised draft answers the following question: How did new technology and innovations affect China, Japan, Korea, and Southeast Asia?

TOPIC 6

Civilizations of the Americas Preview

Essential Question How much does geography shape people's lives?

Before you begin this topic, think about the Essential Question by answering the following questions.

What geographical features are important to your community? Why are they important?

Timeline Skills

As you read, write and/or draw at least three events from the topic. Draw a line from each event to its correct position on the timeline.

1200 BCE	1000 BCE	800 BCE	1000 CE

Map Skills

Using maps throughout the topic, label the outline map with the places listed. Then, color in the areas occupied by the Olmecs, Maya, Aztecs, and Inca.

North America	South America	Tikal	Cuzco
Tenochtitlan	Gulf of Mexico	Lake Texcoco	Lake Titicaca
Amazon River	Caribbean Sea	Atlantic Ocean	Pacific Ocean

1200 CE	1400 CE	1600 CE

Quest
Project-Based Learning Inquiry

Be a Map-Maker

On this Quest, you will need to find out what geographic factors shaped the lives of the Maya, Aztecs, and Incas. You will examine sources from the ancient Americas, and find examples of how geography influenced the development of those civilizations. At the end of the Quest, you will create a variety of illustrated special-purpose maps for each civilization.

① Ask Questions (See Student Text, page 266)

For your project, your team will collect information to create special purpose maps, such as physical, political, resource, transportation, or economic maps. Physical maps show land features such as mountains, rivers, or lakes. Political maps indicate boundaries between territories, or the location of towns/cities. Resource maps show the location and types of natural resources in a region. Transportation maps could show trade routes, roads, or other routes people or goods travel. Economic maps might show the type of economic activities, such as farming or livestock grazing, that occur in a region.

As you begin your Quest, keep in mind the Guiding Question: **What geographic factors shaped the lives of the Maya, Aztecs, and Incas?** and the Essential Question: **How much does geography shape people's lives?**

What other questions do you need to ask in order to answer these questions? Consider the following aspects of life in ancient American civilizations. Two questions are filled in for you. Add at least two questions in each category.

Theme Structure of the Society

Sample questions:

How did the geography of the region influence the organization of the society?

What effect did geography have on achievements in architecture and engineering?

 INTERACTIVE

For extra help with Step 1, review the 21st Century Tutorial: **Read Special Purpose Maps**.

Theme Agriculture and Food

Theme Economy and Trade

Theme Homes and Dwellings

Theme My Additional Questions

> 👆 **INTERACTIVE**
>
> For extra help with Step 1, review the
> 21st Century Tutorial: **Ask Questions**.

Quest CONNECTIONS

❷ Investigate

As you read about the ancient Americas, collect five connections from your text to help you answer the Guiding Question. Three connections are already chosen for you.

Connect to the Mayan Civilization

Lesson 1 Settlement and Geography of the Americas
(See Student Text, page 269)

Here's a connection! The terrain occupied by the Maya varied greatly. What were some of the different environments they lived in?

How do you think geography affected trade across Central America?

136
Civilizations of the Americas

Connect to the Aztec Empire

Lesson 2 Where Did the Aztecs Live? (See Student Text, page 277)

Here's another connection! Examine the development of the Aztec empire. Why were the Aztecs so successful in building such a large empire?

How do you think geography helped them maintain their position?

Connect to Early American Migration

Lesson 3 How Did the Geography of the Andes Shape Life?
(See Student Text, page 284)

What does this connection tell you about how early Americans migrated on foot to find their new homes? What kind of obstacles would they have faced in what is now South America?

What influence do you think these obstacles had on where they ultimately settled and why?

It's Your Turn! **Find two more connections. Fill in the title of your connections, then answer the questions. Connections may be images, primary sources, maps, or text.**

Your Choice | Connect to

Location in text

What is the main idea of this connection?

What does it tell you about how geography shaped the lives of the Maya, Aztecs, and Incas?

Your Choice | Connect to

Location in text

What is the main idea of this connection?

What does it tell you about how geography shaped the lives of the Maya, Aztecs, and Incas?

③ Conduct Research (See Student Text, page 298)

Your team will be assigned a region in either Mesoamerica or South America. Once your region is assigned, decide as a team on three types of maps that you will create. Circle them in the chart below. Then, record which team member(s) will be responsible for each type of map.

You will do research only about the segment assigned to you. Use the ideas in the connections to further explore the type of map you have been assigned. Pick what your map will show, and find more sources about that subject. Remember, you will also need to illustrate your map, so find images that can help you create that type of map. Be sure to find valid sources and take good notes so you can properly cite your sources.

Type of Map	Team Member(s)	What Information Will the Map Show?
Physical		
Political		
Resource		
Transportation		
Economic		

INTERACTIVE

For extra help, review the 21st Century Tutorials: **Work in Teams** and **Search for Information on the Internet**.

4 Create Your Atlas (See Student Text, page 298)

Now it's time to put together all of the information you have gathered to create your three maps.

1. **Prepare to Make Your Map** Review the research you've collected, and make sure the information you've gathered really supports the main purpose of the map you will create. In the space below, write the specific locations, routes, regions, etc. that you will show on your map.

2. **Draw a Draft** Using the illustrations you found in your research, draw or use technology to create a first draft of your map. Make sure that your map includes important map features, such as a title, key, relevant labels, etc.

3. **Share with a Partner** Once you have finished your draft, ask one of your team members to look it over. Revise your map based on your team member's comments, and comment on his or her map, if possible.

4. **Create Your Atlas** Once all the team members have revised their maps, it's time to put them together. You can do this in a couple of ways:
1) by using technology to create a single document or presentation; or
2) by binding your three printed or drawn maps together.
Your teacher will let you know his or her preference for delivery.

5. **Reflect on the Quest** Think about your experience completing this topic's Quest. What did you learn about how geography shaped and affected the lives and development of early American civilizations? What questions do you still have about these civilizations or the geography that influenced them? How will you answer your questions?

Reflections

INTERACTIVE

For extra help with Step 1, review the 21st Century Tutorial: **Create Charts and Maps**.

Take Notes

Literacy Skill: Sequence Use what you have read to complete the chart. In each space, write or draw in sequence the events that led to the rise and fall of the Maya. Be sure to include an important detail about each event. The first one has been completed for you.

- The first people settled in the Americas between 40,000 and 15,000 years ago. They may have walked over the Bering Land Bridge or come by boat.

INTERACTIVE

For extra help, review the 21st Century Tutorials: **Sequence**.

Practice Vocabulary

Words in Context For each question below, write an answer that shows your understanding of the boldfaced key term.

1. How did **slash-and-burn** both help and hurt the populations who used it?

2. What effect did **drought** have on the Mayan civilization?

3. What is a **hieroglyphic**, and why was it important to ancient American civilizations?

4. What is an **observatory**, and why was it an important feature in Mayan cities?

Quick Activity Human Monument Game

With your group, examine some of the major aspects of Mayan civilization. Consider important achievements, such as building remarkable structures in their cities, the Mayan sacred ball game, slash-and-burn agriculture, hieroglyphic writing, and astronomy.

Team Challenge! You have ten minutes to plan your group statue. Decide with your group which of these, or another important feature of Mayan civilization, you would like to showcase. Your group will represent the idea by "freezing" into a statue or scene that represents the aspect of Mayan society or culture you have chosen. Be sure that your idea is recognizable so that other groups can identify what your statue represents!

Lesson 2 The Aztecs

Take Notes

Literacy Skills: Summarize Use what you have read to complete the table. In each space, write three details about the aspect of Aztec life. One example has been provided. Then, use your notes to summarize the lesson.

Environment	Warfare and Rulers	Society and Achievements
1. Building their capital city, Tenochtitlan, on an island in Lake Texcoco, made it easy to defend.	1.	1.
2.	2.	2.
3.	3.	3.

Summary:

For extra help, review the 21st Century Tutorials: **Summarize**.

Copyright © Savvas Learning Company LLC. All Rights Reserved.

TOPIC 6   145   Civilizations of the Americas

Practice Vocabulary

Vocabulary Quiz Show Some quiz shows ask a question and expect the contestant to give the answer. In other shows, the contestant is given an answer and must supply the question. If the blank is in the Question column, write the question that would result in the answer in the Answer column. If the question is supplied, write the answer.

Question

1. What is the name of the engineering structure used to carry water from one place to another?

2.

3. What is a system of government in which one person from a ruling family has unlimited power?

4.

5. What is the term for a bowl-shaped geographic area?

Answer

1.

2. chinampa

3.

4. dike

5.

Take Notes

Literacy Skills: Analyze Text Structure Use what you have read to complete the table. Use the main headings in your text to organize information, and add details to analyze the information offered in each section. Include at least two details under each heading. The first one has been started for you.

Heading	Details
Geography	• The Incas adapted to difficult geography by developing terraces to allow them to farm on the sides of mountains. •

👆 INTERACTIVE

For extra help, review the 21st Century Tutorials: **Take Effective Notes**.

Practice Vocabulary

True or False? Decide whether each statement below is true or false. Circle T or F, and then explain your answer. Be sure to include the underlined vocabulary word in your explanation. The first one is done for you.

1. **T / F** A <u>terrace</u> was where children of the Incas went to play on the swings.
   False. A <u>terrace</u> is a strip of level land cut out of a mountainside for farming.

2. **T / F** A <u>quipu</u> was a device used by the Incas to keep records.

3. **T / F** A <u>hierarchy</u> is a way to carry water up the mountainside.

4. **T / F** An <u>ayllu</u> is the name of an animal similar to a llama or alpaca.

5. **T / F** The Incas paid taxes through the <u>mita system</u>.

Quick Activity Write a Song

Write a song praising the achievements of the Incas.

With a partner, talk about some of your favorite songs. What do they have in common? For example, your favorite songs may have things, such as rhyming, rhythm, and melody, in common.

Team Challenge! Write a short song praising some of the achievements of the Incas. You can use the rhythm or melody of your favorite song, or make up your own.

Use the space provided to make notes and write your song. (Your teacher may ask for volunteers to perform their songs.)

Take Notes

Literacy Skills: Compare and Contrast Use what you have read to complete the table. In each space, write 2-3 facts about how geography affected each broad population. What were the similarities? What were the differences? The first one has been completed for you.

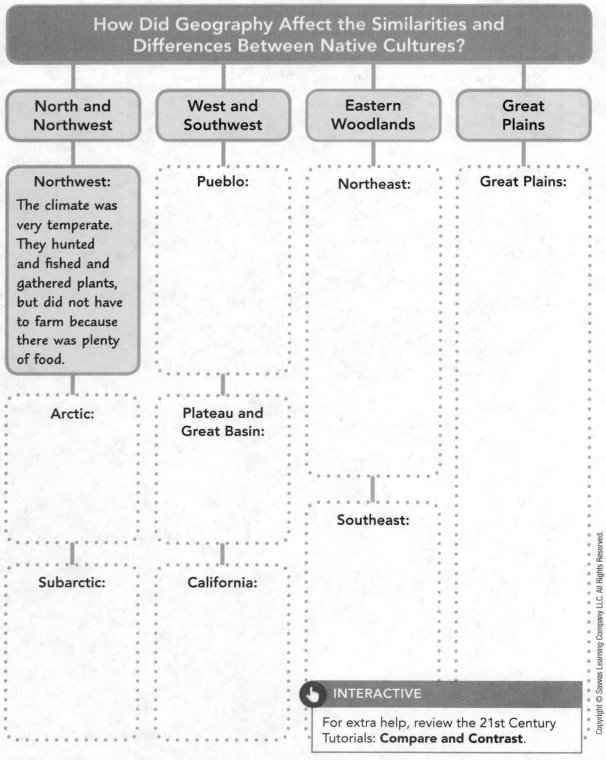

How Did Geography Affect the Similarities and Differences Between Native Cultures?

North and Northwest

West and Southwest

Eastern Woodlands

Great Plains

Northwest:
The climate was very temperate. They hunted and fished and gathered plants, but did not have to farm because there was plenty of food.

Pueblo:

Northeast:

Great Plains:

Arctic:

Plateau and Great Basin:

Southeast:

Subarctic:

California:

INTERACTIVE

For extra help, review the 21st Century Tutorials: **Compare and Contrast**.

Practice Vocabulary

Matching Logic Using your knowledge of the underlined vocabulary words, draw a line from each sentence in Column 1 to match it with the sentence in Column 2 to which it logically belongs.

Column 1	Column 2
1. Native peoples left behind numerous <u>artifacts</u>.	This type of round home was made of tree trunks.
2. Wealthy families hosted <u>potlatches</u> to celebrate important events.	Jewelry, tools, and pottery help us understand what their lives were like.
3. Many native peoples were faced with <u>drought</u>.	These homes were portable and made moving around easier.
4. Some Eastern Woodlands peoples lived in a <u>wigwam</u>.	These were rectangular homes made of tree trunks and covered with bark.
5. Arctic people sometimes lived in <u>igloos</u> during the winter.	These homes made of snow bricks were surprisingly warm.
6. Some native people lived in <u>tepees</u>.	These were also times to share stories about family history and pass down heritage.
7. The Iroquois people lived in <u>longhouses</u>.	Some geographical places get little rain and sometimes none at all.

Writing Workshop Explanatory Essay

As you read, build a response to this topic: **Compare the impact of geography on Mayan, Aztec, and Incan agriculture. The** prompts below will help walk you through the process.

Lesson 1 Writing Task: Develop a Clear Thesis (See Student Text, page 273)

Express in one sentence how you can compare and contrast the impact of geography on Mayan, Aztec, and Incan agriculture. This will be your thesis statement for the explanatory essay you will write at the end of the topic.

Lesson 2 Writing Task: Support Ideas with Evidence
(See Student Text, page 281)

Gather evidence from your text, and use the chart below to record information about the agricultural practices of these cultures so that you can identify differences and similarities.

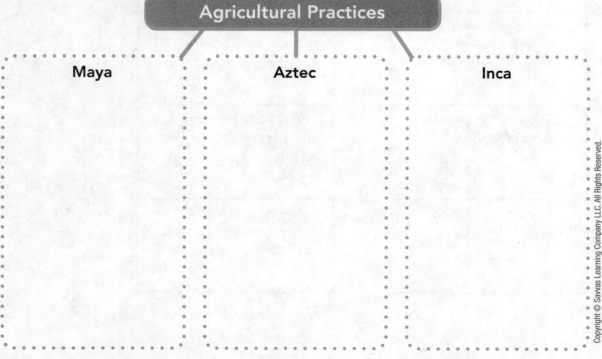

Agricultural Practices

Maya	Aztec	Inca

Lesson 3 Writing Task: Support Thesis with Details
(See Student Text, page 289)

Revisit your evidence chart from Lesson 2. Add any additional details that are important to your thesis statement.

Thesis	
Impact, Evidence, Details	
Impact, Evidence, Details	
Impact, Evidence, Details	
Conclusion	

Lesson 4 Writing Task: Clarify Relationships with Transition Words
(See Student Text, page 297)

Reread the thesis statement and your supporting details. Clarify your writing, using words and phrases to create smooth transitions between different ideas. Use appropriate words to describe similarities and differences.

Writing Task (See Student Text, page 299)

Using the outline you created, respond to the following statement in a five paragraph explanatory essay: **Compare the impact of geography on Mayan, Aztec, and Incan agriculture**. As you write, pay close attention to your signal and transition words to help you compare and contrast effectively.

Essential Question What makes cultures endure?

Before you begin this topic, think about the Essential Question by completing the following activity.

1. List five elements of culture that you have experienced in your family or in your community. Next to each element, write how you learned about or first experienced it.

2. Preview the topic by skimming the images and captions in the lessons. Then place a check mark next to the elements of culture that are physical things made by people.

__architecture   __holidays   __masks   __songs

__religious ritual __celebrations __musical instruments __traditional dress

Timeline Skills

As you read, write and/or draw at least three events from the topic. Draw a line from each event to its correct position on the timeline.

500
CE

750
CE

Map Skills

Using maps throughout the topic, label the outline map with the places listed.
Then color in significant physical features, such as desert, mountain ranges,
savannah, and rainforest. Add the colors and their meanings to a map key.

Axum	Koumbi Saleh	Benin	Meroe
Mediterranean Sea	Red Sea	Timbuktu	Nile River
Atlantic Ocean	Sahara	Indian Ocean	

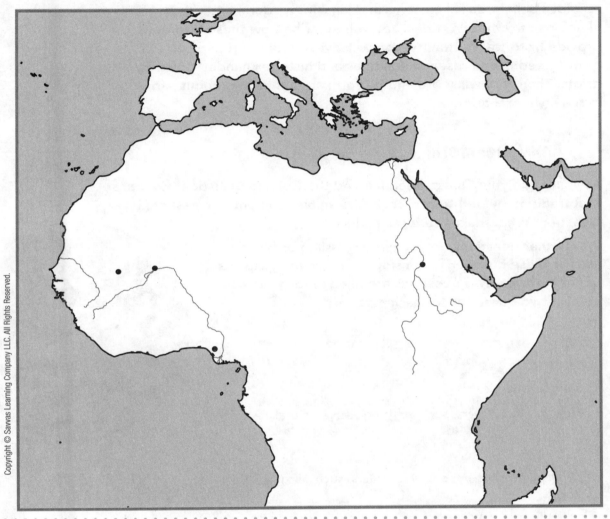

1000	1250	1500
CE	CE	CE

Quest

Project-Based Learning

Create an Oral History

On this Quest, you will explore how oral traditions preserve history, religious beliefs, social customs and kinship, wisdom, and other elements of culture in Africa. You will describe how these traditions provide historical continuity. You will investigate the role of the griot (greeoh), and research folktales and histories handed down by griots. Then, you will write and perform an oral history about Africa in the style of a griot.

① Ask Questions (See Student Text, page 304)

As you begin your Quest, keep in mind the Guiding Question: **How has oral tradition helped to preserve African history?** and the Essential Question: **What makes cultures endure?**

What other questions do you need to ask in order to answer these questions? Consider the following aspects of life in Africa. Two questions are filled in for you. Add at least two questions for each category.

Theme History

Sample questions:

How did storytellers, such as griots, serve as oral historians?

Why were griots important to rulers, such as kings?

Theme Religion

Theme Society and Economy

Theme Culture

Theme My Additional Questions

INTERACTIVE

For extra help with Step 1, review the
21st Century Tutorial: **Ask Questions**.

Quest CONNECTIONS

2 Investigate

As you read about civilizations in Africa, collect five connections from your text to help you answer the Guiding Question. Three connections are already chosen for you.

Connect to Al-Bakri's Story

Lesson 1 The Growth of the Ghana Empire (See Student Text, page 309)

Here's a connection! Read the excerpt from a story by Al-Bakri, a historian and geographer who recorded information about the kingdom of Ghana in the 1000s. About whom does Al-Bakri write? What does his story suggest about the ruling class of Ghana? What insights into Ghana's culture does the excerpt offer?

How do accounts like this help preserve African history and culture?

Connect to the Story About Ananse

Lesson 4 What are Key Features of Africa's Cultural Legacy?
(See Student Text, page 326)

Here's another connection! Ananse is a popular trickster character in African folklore. Griots often tell stories like this one. What does the story suggest about how people obtain wisdom? What does the story reveal about African values?

How do stories like this one help preserve African history and culture?

Connect to the Griot's Story Tale Sundiata

Primary Sources Djibril Tamsir Niane, Sundiata: An Epic of Old Mali
(See Student Text, page 328)

What does this connection tell about Sundiata, the first king of Mali in the 1200s? How does the story describe Sundiata as a child? What does this tale reflect about the kingship of Mali? What ideas about life does the story reveal?

How does oral tradition like this griot's tale help preserve African history and culture?

It's Your Turn! **Find two more connections. Fill in the titles of your connections, then answer the questions. Connections may be images, primary sources, maps, or text.**

Your Choice | Connect to

Location in text

What is the main idea of this connection?

What does it tell you about how African history and culture have been preserved?

Your Choice | Connect to

Location in text

What is the main idea of this connection?

What does it tell you about how African history and culture have been preserved?

③ Conduct Research (See Student Text, page 330)

As a group, decide whether to research either folktales or an historical event.

- For folktales, research the background and nature of the type of folktales, including the geographic area in which such tales originated or were commonly told. Read at least three examples of this type of folktale. Summarize each in the chart below, including its origin, message, and how dialogue, tone, plot, and setting help get across the meaning.

- For history, research the major historical events of the selected civilization. Choose one notable event or period to further investigate. Record information about the event in the chart below.

Folk Tales	Historical Event
Summary of Folktale 1	What happened in the event you've chosen?
Summary of Folktale 2	Who played an important role in this event?
Summary of Folktale 3	Why is it important to remember this event?

👆 INTERACTIVE

For extra help with Step 3, review the 21st Century Tutorial: **Analyze Primary and Secondary Sources**.

Quest FINDINGS

4 Present Your Oral History (See Student Text, page 330)

Now it's time to put together all of the information you have gathered and perform your oral history.

1. **Prepare to Write** You have collected connections that show how oral history traditions help preserve African history and culture. You have also researched a specific type of folktale or specific event in African history. Look through your notes and work with your group to decide on the elements to include in your oral history presentation. Record the elements you want to include here.

Outline of Elements

2. Write a Draft Using the primary sources that you read as models, write a draft of the oral history. For a folktale-based project, highlight important elements of culture. Recall how the folktales that you read centered on specific characters and used dialogue, tone, plot, and setting to convey meaning. Incorporate these things into your story. For a history-based project, focus on the most important people and actions, and emphasize how your piece of history fits into the broader story of Africa.

3. Share and Edit the Draft Have the writers combine and share their drafts with the editors. Editors should check the draft against the groups' element notes to be sure that the oral history includes all the relevant information. They should also ask themselves broad questions about the drafts, such as "What will the audience learn from this oral history? What does this oral history say about African history or culture?" Editors should advise revisions, if needed, based on these considerations. They should tell the writers what they like about the draft as well as what parts need improvement. Be sure that editors read aloud the draft to hear how the oral history flows. After all, the final draft will be performed!

4. Finalize and Present Your Oral History Have editors and writers work together to revise the draft. Then, have the presenters practice reading aloud the oral history to the rest of the group. Group members who are not presenting should provide feedback on the presentation. Presenters should speak clearly, at a moderate pace. Consider adding a musical background. Finally, have presenters perform their oral history for the class.

5. Reflect on the Quest Think about your experience completing this topic's Quest and watching other groups' presentations. What did you learn about the oral history traditions of African civilizations?

Reflections

Take Notes

Literacy Skills: Summarize Use what you have read to complete the concept webs. Summarize what you learned, in one to two sentences, for each section in the webs. The first one has been started for you.

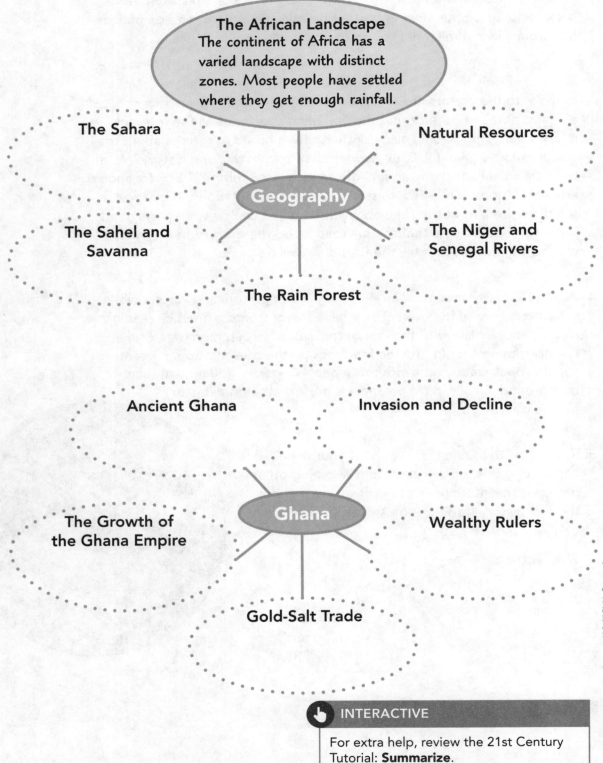

The African Landscape
The continent of Africa has a varied landscape with distinct zones. Most people have settled where they get enough rainfall.

The Sahara

Natural Resources

Geography

The Sahel and Savanna

The Niger and Senegal Rivers

The Rain Forest

Ancient Ghana

Invasion and Decline

Ghana

The Growth of the Ghana Empire

Wealthy Rulers

Gold-Salt Trade

INTERACTIVE

For extra help, review the 21st Century Tutorial: **Summarize**.

Practice Vocabulary

Vocabulary Quiz Show Some quiz shows ask a question and expect the contestant to give the answer. In other shows, the contestant is given an answer and must supply the question. If the blank is in the Question column, write the question that would result in the answer in the Answer column. If the question is supplied, write the answer.

Question

1. What do you call the raised area of largely flat land that makes up much of Africa's interior?

2.

3. What are land, trees, and minerals called when they are used by people to meet their needs?

4.

5. What do you call the trade in gold and salt that took place between North African peoples and West African peoples?

6.

Answer

1.

2. This vast region of tropical grassland covers much of Sub-Saharan Africa.

3.

4. This happens when people become experts in specific skills or jobs, like farming, government service, mining, or crafts.

5.

6. Beginning in the 900s, Arab and Berber merchants traversed the Sahara in these camel-mounted groups.

Quick Activity Packing for the Caravan

With a partner, study the map. Consider what the journey from one city to the next would have been like. Use the scale to determine the distance between several urban centers. If a camel caravan, loaded with goods, averages about 20 miles a day, how long would it take to travel between each pair of cities? Compare your findings with those of another pair of students.

Did you know?

Generally, the Sahara Desert receives less than 4 in. of rainfall per year.

Temperatures during the day often reach over 100°F and can drop below 0°F at night.

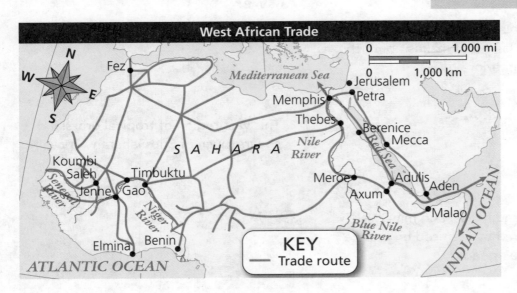

West African Trade

KEY
— Trade route

INTERACTIVE

For extra help, review the 21st Century Tutorial: **Use Parts of a Map**.

Team Challenge! What would you pack to travel with a caravan from Timbuktu to Fez? With your group, brainstorm a checklist, or manifest, of what you would take. Remember that you are traveling in a trading caravan, so you will need goods for trading as well as supplies. Display completed lists on large sheets of paper around the class. Study each list, and point out potential problems or make suggestions.

Take Notes

Literacy Skills: Sequence Use what you have read to complete the timeline. In the spaces provided, write key events in the development of the Mali and Songhai empires. The first one has been completed for you.

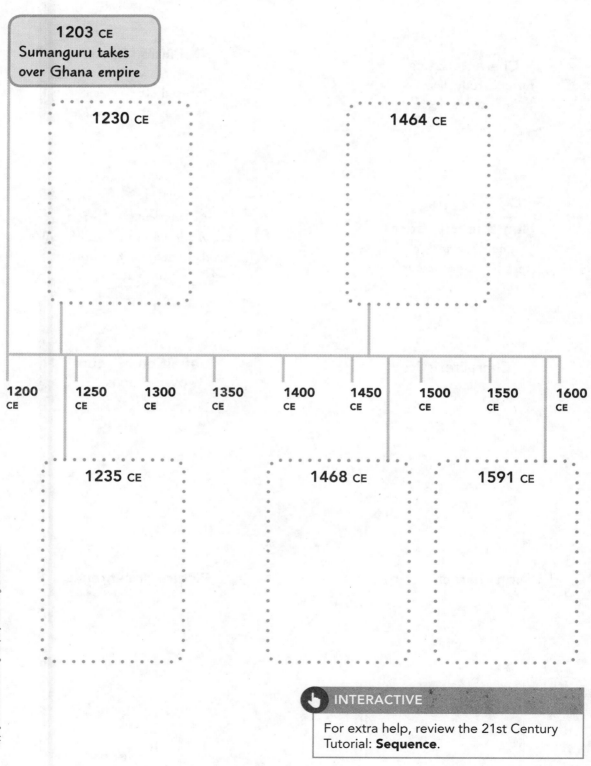

1203 CE
Sumanguru takes over Ghana empire

1230 CE

1464 CE

1200 CE   1250 CE   1300 CE   1350 CE   1400 CE   1450 CE   1500 CE   1550 CE   1600 CE

1235 CE

1468 CE

1591 CE

INTERACTIVE

For extra help, review the 21st Century Tutorial: **Sequence**.

Practice Vocabulary

Word Map Study the word map for the word *scholarship*. Characteristics are words or phrases that relate to the word in the center of the word map. Non-characteristics are words and phrases not associated with the word. Use the blank word map to explore the meaning of the word *griot*.

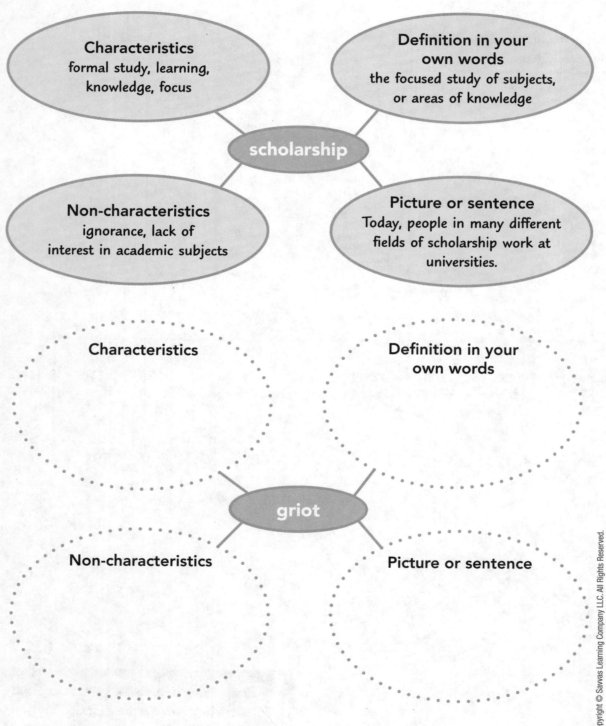

Characteristics
formal study, learning, knowledge, focus

Definition in your own words
the focused study of subjects, or areas of knowledge

scholarship

Non-characteristics
ignorance, lack of interest in academic subjects

Picture or sentence
Today, people in many different fields of scholarship work at universities.

Characteristics

Definition in your own words

griot

Non-characteristics

Picture or sentence

Quick Activity Perspectives on West African Kingdoms

When you read primary sources, it is important to keep in mind the perspective from which a source is written. Perspective refers to the way in which a person sees and understands a subject. Think about a recent disagreement you had. Your perspective on the issue probably differs from the perspective of the person with whom you disagreed. An author's perspective influences what the author writes. In a small group, take turns reading aloud the primary sources below. Make a chart or web in which you record the main ideas of each excerpt. Consider these questions as you take notes: How does each author write about West Africa? What feelings, or bias, does each author show? What overall impression does each author give of West African kingdoms?

> "In their new-found peace the villages knew prosperity again, for with Sundiata happiness had come into everyone's home. Vast fields of millet, rice, cotton, indigo and fonio surrounded the villages. Whoever worked always had something to live on. Each year long caravans carried the taxes in kind to Niani. You could go from village to village without fearing brigands. A thief would have his right hand chopped off and if he stole again he would be put to the sword."
>
> —from *The Epic of Sundiata*, as handed down by West African griots and told by their descendent, Djibril Tamsir Niane

> "A traveller in this country carries nothing but pieces of salt and glass ornaments, which the people call beads, and some sweet-smelling goods. When he comes to a village the womenfolk . . . bring out millet, milk, chickens, pulped lotus fruit, rice, and pounded haricot beans. The traveller buys what he wants of these."
>
> —from the writings of the fourteenth century Moroccan scholar Ibn Battuta

> "This king is the greatest of the Muslim kings of the Sahel. He rules the most extensive territory, has the most numerous army, is the bravest, the richest, the most fortunate, the most victorious over his enemies, and the best able to distribute benefits."
>
> —from the fourteenth century Syrian Arab historian al-Umari

Team Challenge! Compare and contrast the perspectives of the three authors. How might the authors' backgrounds affect their perspective of West African kings and kingdoms? Write down your ideas and share with your group.

 INTERACTIVE

For extra help, review the 21st Century Tutorials: **Compare Viewpoints** and **Identify Bias**.

Take Notes

Literacy Skills: Identify Cause and Effect Use what you have read to complete the cause-event-effect charts. For each chart, record the cause(s) and effect(s) of the listed events. The first one has been completed for you.

Cause(s)	King Ezana of Axum took over Kush.
Event	After many generations, the rule of Kushite kings weakened.
Effect(s)	Axum gained control of trade routes to Roman Egypt, southern Arabia, and Asia, and grew prosperous.

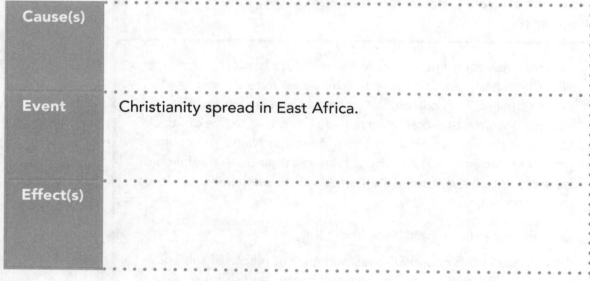

Cause(s)	
Event	Christianity spread in East Africa.
Effect(s)	

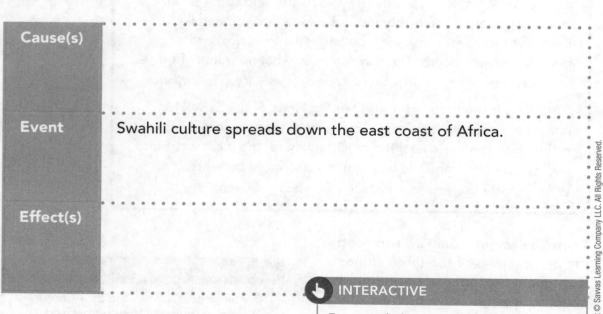

Cause(s)	
Event	Swahili culture spreads down the east coast of Africa.
Effect(s)	

👆 INTERACTIVE

For extra help, review the 21st Century Tutorial: **Analyze Cause and Effect**.

Practice Vocabulary

True or False? Decide whether each statement below is true or false. Circle T or F, and then explain your answer. Be sure to include the underlined vocabulary word in your explanation. The first one is done for you.

1. **T / F** <u>Monks</u> prevented the adoption of Christianity by people in Axum and other African kingdoms.
   False; <u>Monks</u> helped spread Christianity to people in Axum and other African kingdoms.

2. **T / F** Monumental <u>stele</u> marked the burial places of Axum's rulers.

3. **T / F** The people of Axum benefited from trade with <u>Greco-Roman</u> outposts along the Red Sea and the Mediterranean Sea.

4. **T / F** Ruling <u>dynasties</u> in Ethiopia ensured that no one family came to dominate the rule of the kingdom.

5. **T / F** Swahili <u>stonetowns</u> in East Africa remained largely isolated from non-African cultures.

Take Notes

Literacy Skills: Integrate Visual Information Use what you have read and studied in the lesson's visual aids to complete the charts. In each space provided, record important details about the topics of each section. Be sure to include information gained from the infographic and photographs in your charts. The first one has been completed for you.

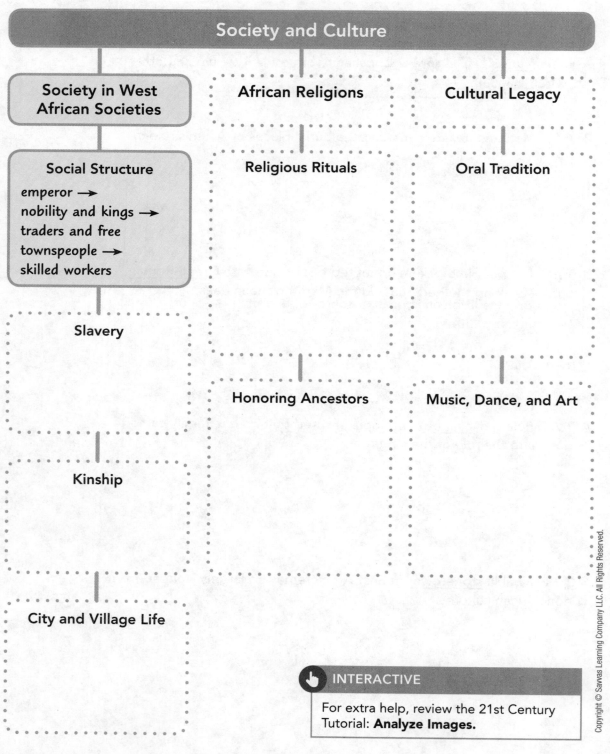

Society and Culture

Society in West African Societies

Social Structure

emperor →
nobility and kings →
traders and free
townspeople →
skilled workers

Slavery

Kinship

City and Village Life

African Religions

Religious Rituals

Honoring Ancestors

Cultural Legacy

Oral Tradition

Music, Dance, and Art

👆 INTERACTIVE

For extra help, review the 21st Century Tutorial: **Analyze Images.**

Practice Vocabulary

Words in Context For each question below, write an answer that shows your understanding of the **boldfaced** key term.

1. What role did **caste** play in West African empires?

2. How were **kinship** and **lineage** related in West African society?

3. What characteristics defined **ethnic groups** within West African empires?

4. Why is **oral tradition** an important source of information about West African cultures?

5. Why did West African griots learn and share **proverbs**?

6. How does **polyrhythmic drumming** affect performers who dance to the music?

173

Writing Workshop Explanatory Essay

As you read, build a response to this question: **How did the environment affect the development of African empires and the trade networks that connected them to other lands, including Europe and Asia?** The prompts below will help walk you through the process.

Lesson 1 Writing Task: Develop a Clear Thesis (See Student Text, page 310)

Express in one sentence how environmental conditions affected the empire of Ghana and the development of trading networks in the region. This will be your thesis statement for the explanatory essay you will write at the end of the topic. Re-read your thesis statement after you read Lessons 2 and 3 and make any revisions needed to include the new information.

Lesson 2 Writing Task: Support Thesis with Details
(See Student Text, page 316)

Now add details from Lessons 1 and 2 to support your thesis statement. Update your chart after you read Lessons 3 and 4 as well.

Lesson 1	
Lesson 2	
Lesson 3	
Lesson 4	

Lesson 3 Writing Task: Pick an Organizing Strategy

(See Student Text, page 322)

Think about what type of organization suits your essay. Sometimes the phrasing of the writing prompt can provide a clue. In this writing prompt, the word *affect* is used. Your essay should tell the effects of geography on Ghana and Mali, so an organization in which you explain multiple effects would be a good way to go. Make an outline of your essay. Start with an introduction, followed by three paragraphs that explain key effects and end with a conclusion. Use the chart below to help you.

Introduction Thesis	
Effect 1 Evidence	
Effect 2 Evidence	
Effect 3 Evidence	
Conclusion	

Lesson 4 Writing Task: Consider Your Purpose and Audience

(See Student Text, page 327)

With a partner, share your outline, your thesis statement, and the supporting evidence that you recorded from Lessons 1 through 4. Discuss whether your outline includes all of the relevant information you recorded. Then comment on your partner's outline.

Writing Task (See Student Text, page 331)

Using the outline you created in Lesson 3 and revised in Lesson 4, answer the following question in a five-paragraph explanatory essay: How did the environment affect the development of African empires and the trade networks that connected them to other lands, including Europe and Asia? As you write, remember to include a main idea with supporting details in each paragraph.

8 The Renaissance and Reformation Preview

Essential Question How do ideas grow and spread?

Before you begin this topic, think about the Essential Question by completing the following activity.

1. The Renaissance, Reformation, and Scientific Revolution led to the spread of new ways of thinking about all aspects of life. List five ways in which you share ideas and learn, or pick up on new ideas. Keep in mind that such ideas might relate to any aspect of life, including family, community, government, science, religion, and economics.

Timeline Skills

As you read, write and/or draw at least three events from the topic. Draw a line from each event to its correct position on the timeline.

1400	1500

Map Skills

Using maps throughout the topic, label the outline map with the places listed. Then color in bodies of water as well as the boundaries of the German States, Papal States, and Italian city-states, such as the Kingdom of Naples.

German States	Papal States	Venice	Florence
Naples	Rome	Wittenberg	Warburg
Nuremberg	Augsburg	North Sea	Adriatic Sea
Mediterranean Sea	Atlantic Ocean		

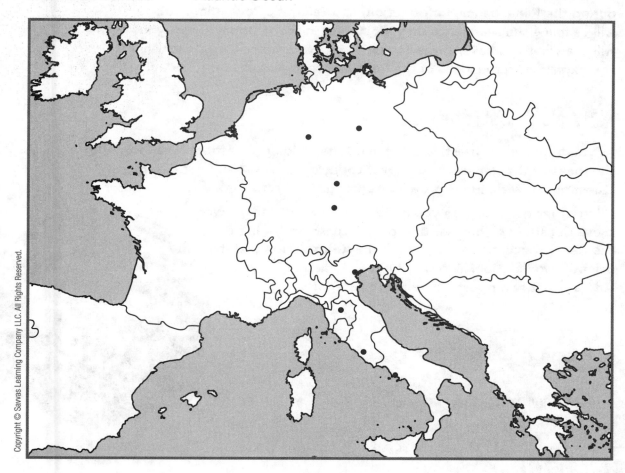

1600

Quest
Document-Based Writing Inquiry

Learning Through the Ages

On this Quest, you will explore primary and secondary sources about the ideas developed by artists, authors, and scientists who lived during the Renaissance, Reformation, and Scientific Revolution. You will examine their influence on your studies in school today. Then, you will use what you have learned to write an explanatory essay in which you explain how the ideas of the Renaissance impact students today.

1 Ask Questions (See Student Text, page 340)

As you begin your Quest, keep in mind the Guiding Question: **How do the ideas of the Renaissance impact today's students?** and the Essential Question: **How do ideas grow and spread?**

What other questions do you need to ask in order to answer these questions? Consider the following aspects of life during the Renaissance, as well as during the Reformation and the Scientific Revolution. Two questions are filled in for you. Add at least two questions for each category.

Theme Art and Architecture

Sample questions:

• How did Renaissance artists change their approach to art?

• What elements of art from the Renaissance still influence us today?

Theme Literature and Literacy

Theme Religion and Philosophy

Theme Government and Society

Theme Science and Technology

Theme My Additional Questions

 INTERACTIVE

For extra help with Step 1, review the
21st Century Tutorial: **Ask Questions**.

Quest CONNECTIONS

② Investigate

As you read about the Renaissance, the Reformation, and the Scientific Revolution, collect five connections from your text to help you answer the Guiding Question. Three connections are already chosen for you.

Connect to Education

Lesson 1 Education in the Liberal Arts (See Student Text, page 345)

Here's a connection! Study the infographic. Which subjects of study were valued during the Renaissance? How did they compare to subjects studied during the Middle Ages?

How do these subjects compare to the subjects you and other students study today?

Connect to John Calvin

Lesson 4 In-Text Primary Source John Calvin, *Institutes of the Christian Religion* (See Student Text, page 365)

Here's another connection! Read the quotation. What does this connection suggest about Calvin's view on the purpose of education? Explain whether you agree or disagree with him.

How does this idea compare to modern views of education in the United States?

Connect to The Scientific Revolution

Lesson 6 The Scientific Method (See Student Text, page 381)

Here's another connection! Study the diagram. What steps does it show for the scientific method?

Do these steps reflect the way you learn about science in school?

Now it's your turn! **Find two more connections on your own. Fill in the title of your connections, then answer the questions. Connections may be images, primary sources, maps, or text.**

Your Choice | Connect to

Location in text

What is the main idea of this connection?

What does it tell you about how Renaissance ideas influenced the subjects you learn today?

Your Choice | Connect to

Location in text

What is the main idea of this connection?

What does it tell you about how Renaissance ideas influenced the subjects you learn today?

3 Examine Primary and Secondary Sources

(See Student Text, page 384)

Examine the primary and secondary sources provided online or that your teacher hands out. Fill in the chart to show how these sources provide further information about how Renaissance ideas influenced modern ideas and education. The first one is completed for you.

NICCOLO MACCHIAVELLI

Source	What Renaissance ideas from these sources remain important today?
"On Noble Customs and Liberal Studies of Adolescents"	Learning must begin at an early age and continue throughout life.
Illustration from *The Nuremberg Chronicle*	
Oration on the Dignity of Man	
Letter to Augustinus Aemilius	
Plate from *On the Fabric of the Human Body*	

INTERACTIVE

For extra help with Step 3, review the 21st Century Tutorials: **Analyze Primary and Secondary Sources** and **Analyze Images**.

4 Write Your Explanatory Essay (See Student Text, page 384)

Now it's time to put together all of the information you have gathered and use it to write your explanatory essay in response to the Guiding Question: **How do the ideas of the Renaissance impact today's students?**

1. **Prepare to Write** You have collected connections and explored primary and secondary sources that show the lasting influence of Renaissance ideas about knowledge and education. Look through your notes, and identify the most important ideas that you want to include in your essay. Record your ideas in the table below. Be sure to write the source of each note.

Renaissance Ideas About Education, including Subjects Studied	
Modern Ideas About Education, including Subjects Studied	
Potential Benefits of Ideas and Subjects	

2. Write a Thesis Statement Review your notes in the table. What main idea ties together all the information? Write a one-sentence thesis statement in response to the Guiding Question.

....

3. Write a Draft On a separate sheet of paper organize your notes in an outline. Then, use your outline to write a draft of your explanatory essay. Remember to include your thesis statement and at least three paragraphs with evidence to support that statement. Your evidence should reference the sources and connections that you explored during the Quest.

4. Revise and Finalize Your Essay Share your completed draft with a partner. Take turns providing feedback to each other. Ask yourselves if each essay answers the Guiding Question clearly and cites appropriate evidence. Correct any grammatical or spelling errors. Then, finalize your essay.

5. Reflect on the Quest Think about your experience completing this topic's Quest. What did you learn about the influence of Renaissance ideas on modern schools? What questions do you still have about the lasting legacy of the Renaissance? How will you answer them?

 INTERACTIVE

For extra help with Step 4, review the 21st Century Tutorial: **Write an Essay**.

Take Notes

Literacy Skills: Analyze Cause and Effect Use what you have read to complete the chart. Record causes that led to the listed effects of the Renaissance. The first one has been completed for you.

Causes	Effect
• Trade and industry increased. • Towns grew. • Both peasants and nobles moved to towns.	Feudalism and manorialism weakened.
• • •	The Renaissance first developed in Italian city-states.
•	Florence became a center of Renaissance culture.
• •	Church power and influence declined.
• •	Renaissance ideas spread across Europe.
• •	

INTERACTIVE

For extra help, review the 21st Century Tutorial: **Analyze Cause and Effect**.

Practice Vocabulary

Word Map Study the word map for the word *mercantile*. Characteristics are words or phrases that relate to the word in the center of the word map. Non-characteristics are words and phrases not associated with the word. Use the blank word map to explore the meaning of the word *Renaissance*. Then make word maps of your own for these words: *patron, humanism, secularism, vernacular, individualism, satire,* and *utopia*.

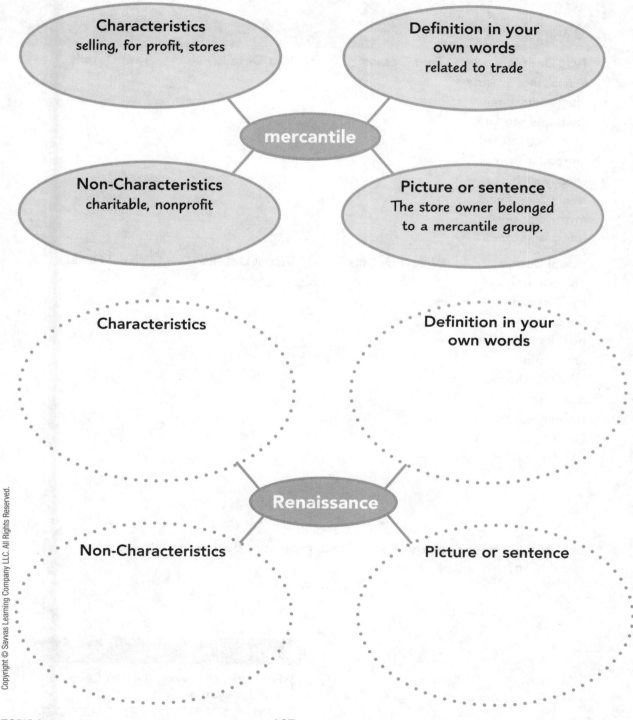

Characteristics
selling, for profit, stores

Definition in your own words
related to trade

mercantile

Non-Characteristics
charitable, nonprofit

Picture or sentence
The store owner belonged to a mercantile group.

Characteristics

Definition in your own words

Renaissance

Non-Characteristics

Picture or sentence

Take Notes

Literacy Skills: Integrate Visual Information Use what you have read to complete the table. Beneath each heading, list key details from the lesson text, as well as from the primary source art and other images. Then, use your notes to synthesize what you learned from text and visual sources of information in the lesson. The first one has been partially filled in for you.

An Artistic Revolution	Great Artists of the Renaissance	Architecture Advances	Renaissance Literature
Text Details Renaissance artists often blended religious and secular themes or focused on secular themes entirely such as scenes from Greek mythology, portraits, landscapes.	**Text Details**	**Text Details**	**Text Details**
Visual Details The painting by Benozzo Gozzoli shows how Renaissance artists mix religious themes and realistic technique. • •	**Visual Details**	**Visual Details**	**Visual Details**

Synthesize: How does the Renaissance represent both a rebirth and a revolution?

👆 INTERACTIVE

For extra help, review the 21st Century Tutorial: **Synthesize.**

Practice Vocabulary

Words in Context For each question below, write an answer that shows your understanding of the **boldfaced** key term.

1. What kind of story does a **picaresque** novel tell?

2. What does **linear perspective** allow artists to do?

3. What are the characteristics of a **sonnet**?

4. How does **proportion** help architects to make pleasing designs?

5. How does an artist make an **engraving**?

Quick Activity Drawing in 3D

Leonardo da Vinci, like other Renaissance artists, used linear perspective to show depth and distance in his paintings. With a partner, research some of his paintings, such as *The Last Supper* or *The Annunciation*, and discuss what gives the paintings a sense of depth.

Da Vinci's paintings often had a vanishing point, to which your eye is naturally drawn, and a horizontal line, called the *horizon line*, that divides the top part of the image from the bottom. The perspective grid below provides a horizon line, a vanishing point, and other lines of perspective.

Did you know?

Before the 1400s, artists did not know how to draw or paint objects on flat surfaces the way the eye actually sees them. Using geometry to show perspective changed that.

Team Challenge! Sit or stand across from a partner. Use the perspective grid to draw your partner and the surrounding environment. Begin by sketching your partner at the vanishing point. Then, add objects and people that appear on each side of him or her. Keep in mind that the farther away an object is, the smaller it appears. Use the lines on the grid to help. Generally, the sides of things will run straight up and down, while the tops and bottoms will angle toward the vanishing point. When you have finished, compare your 3D drawings!

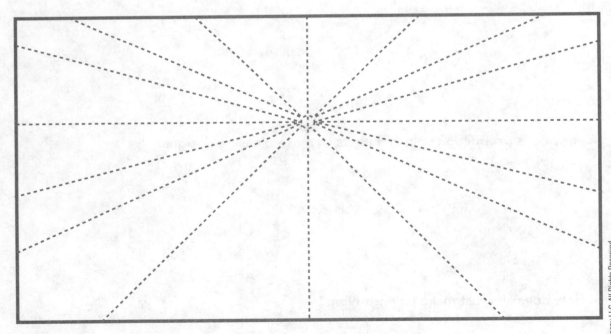

Take Notes

Literacy Skills: Identify Main Idea and Details Use what you have read
to complete the charts. Write two main ideas from the lesson text.
Then, list supporting details from the text for each main idea. The
first one has been completed for you.

Main Idea
Renaissance culture changed the ways in which people thought about the
world and shared ideas.

Detail

Authors began writing
more books in the
vernacular, increasing
literacy.

Detail

Detail

Main Idea

Detail

Detail

Detail

INTERACTIVE

For extra help, review the 21st Century
Tutorial: **Identify Main Ideas and Details**.

Practice Vocabulary

Word Map Study the word map for the term *movable type*. Characteristics are words or phrases that relate to the term in the center of the word map. Non-characteristics are words and phrases not associated with the term. Use the blank word map to explore the meaning of the word *censor*. Then make a word map of your own for the word *recant*.

Characteristics
Johann Gutenberg, printing press, metal type, individual letters, fast, many pages, less costly

Definition in your own words
individual letters made from metal that can be arranged and rearranged quickly to form words and sentences on a page

movable type

Non-Characteristics
block printing, handwritten, manuscript, wood blocks, slow, page by page, expensive

Picture or sentence
Movable type printing made it faster and easier to produce books.

Characteristics

Definition in your own words

censor

Non-Characteristics

Picture or sentence

Take Notes

Literacy Skills: Summarize Use what you have read to complete the chart. Write the actions associated with the movement in the center.

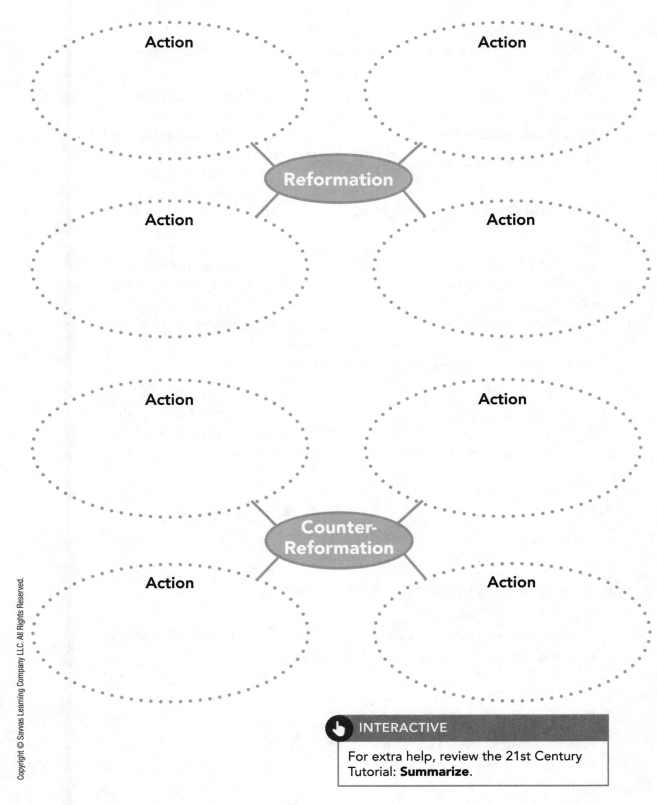

INTERACTIVE

For extra help, review the 21st Century
Tutorial: **Summarize**.

Practice Vocabulary

Sentence Builder Finish the sentences below with a key word from this section. You may have to change the form of the words to complete the sentences.

Word Bank

ghetto	indulgence	predestination	Reformation
sacrament	sect	theocracy	

1. People who believe in .... think that God decided long ago who would gain salvation.

2. During the Counter-Reformation, Venice created a .... to isolate Jews from the rest of the city.

3. Geneva was considered a .... under John Calvin, because religious leaders governed the city.

4. Luther objected to the sale of .... because he believed people could not buy forgiveness or salvation.

5. During the ...., Martin Luther and John Calvin founded Christian churches.

6. The spread of Luther's ideas increased the number of .... in Europe, which means that many different types of Protestant churches sprang up.

7. Luther rejected five out of seven ...., including confession, as unnecessary for salvation.

Quick Activity Who Wrote What?

In this lesson, you have learned about historical figures who ignited the Protestant Reformation as well as leaders of the Catholic Church who responded with the Counter-Reformation. Read the excerpts below. Match the excerpt to one of the individuals listed, and explain your reasoning.

John Calvin   Ignatius of Loyola   Pope Innocent IV

Martin Luther   Pope Paul III   Teresa of Avila

"[W]ith God going before us in our deliberations, and holding before our minds the light of His own wisdom and truth,—we may, ... deliberate and discuss, execute and bring to the desired issue, speedily and happily, ... the integrity and truth of the Christian religion; the restoration of good and the correction of evil manners; the peace, unity, and concord both of Christian princes and peoples; and whatsoever is needful for repelling those assaults of barbarians and infidels, with which they seek the overthrow of all Christendom."

"In conformity, therefore, to the clear doctrine of the Scripture, we assert, that by an eternal and immutable counsel, God has once for all determined, both whom He would admit to salvation, and whom He would condemn to destruction. We affirm that this counsel, as far as concerns the elect, is founded on His gratuitous mercy, totally irrespective of human merit."

"And so it will profit nothing that the body should be adorned with sacred vestments, or dwell in holy places, or be occupied in sacred offices, or pray, fast, and abstain from certain meats, or do whatever works can be done through the body and in the body. ... [T]he soul can do without everything, except the word of God, without which none at all of its wants are provided for."

Team Challenge! Find a student with different matches. Discuss your ideas, and try to come to an agreement on the matches. Note that there are more people listed than you will have matches.

Take Notes

Literacy Skills: Sequence Use what you have read to complete the timeline. Record details about events that took place as a result of the Protestant Reformation. Be sure to draw a line from each box to the appropriate location on the timeline. The first one has been completed for you.

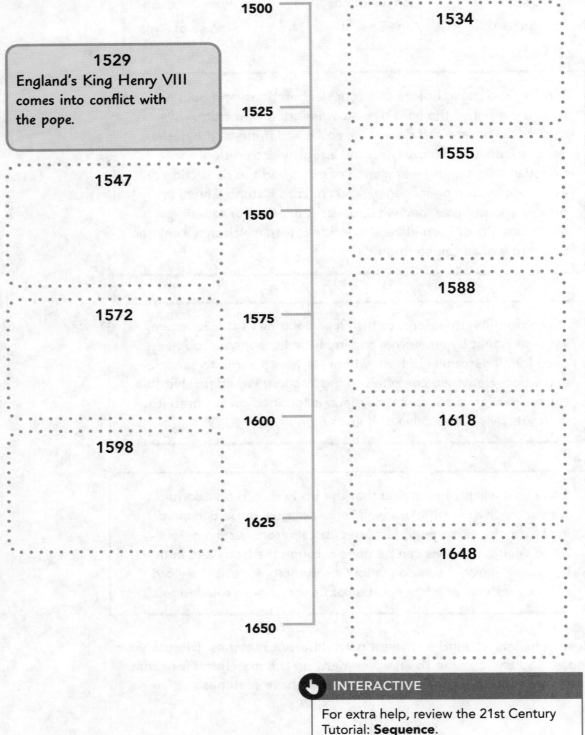

1529
England's King Henry VIII comes into conflict with the pope.

1547

1572

1598

1500

1525

1550

1575

1600

1625

1650

1534

1555

1588

1618

1648

INTERACTIVE

For extra help, review the 21st Century Tutorial: **Sequence**.

Practice Vocabulary

Matching Logic Using your knowledge of the underlined vocabulary words, draw a line from each sentence in Column 1 to match it with the sentence in Column 2 to which it logically belongs.

Column 1	Column 2
1. King Henry VIII split from the Catholic Church when the pope refused to grant him an <u>annulment</u>.	The resulting battle, and loss, ended Spanish control of the seas.
2. Henry IV became king and issued the <u>Edict</u> of Nantes.	He officially declared the Catholic Church to be the church of France and granted French Huguenots the freedom to practice their religion.
3. King Philip sent an <u>armada</u> to attack England.	Such ideas entrusted greater power to local government.
4. Johannes Althusius drew on Calvinist ideas when he developed the idea of <u>federalism</u>.	He ended his marriage and started the Church of England.

Take Notes

Literacy Skills: Identify Main Idea and Details Use what you have read
to complete the table. For each main idea, write details that support it.
The first one has been partially filled in for you.

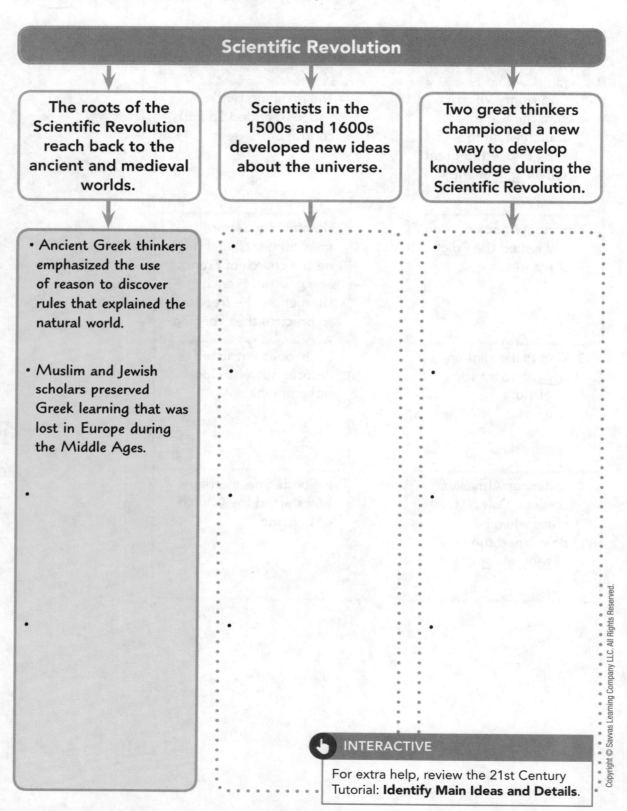

Scientific Revolution

The roots of the Scientific Revolution reach back to the ancient and medieval worlds.

Scientists in the 1500s and 1600s developed new ideas about the universe.

Two great thinkers championed a new way to develop knowledge during the Scientific Revolution.

- Ancient Greek thinkers emphasized the use of reason to discover rules that explained the natural world.

- Muslim and Jewish scholars preserved Greek learning that was lost in Europe during the Middle Ages.

-

-

INTERACTIVE

For extra help, review the 21st Century
Tutorial: **Identify Main Ideas and Details**.

Practice Vocabulary

Vocabulary Quiz Show Some quiz shows ask a question and expect the contestant to give the answer. In other shows, the contestant is given an answer and must supply the question. If the blank is in the Question column, write the question that would result in the answer in the Answer column. If the question is supplied, write the answer.

Question	Answer
1.	1. rationalism
2.	2. heliocentric theory
3. What is a belief that goes against the teaching of the Church called?	3.
4.	4. inductive reasoning
5. What process is followed by using observation, experiments, and careful reasoning to gain new knowledge?	5.
6. What is the theory that all knowledge is gained through experience and by making observations using the senses?	6.

Writing Workshop Research Paper

As you read, gather information on a selected figure from the Renaissance, the Reformation, or the Scientific Revolution. Then, build a response to this question: **How did this individual contribute to the spread of new ideas in Europe?** The prompts below will help walk you through the process.

Lessons 1 and 2 Writing Task: Generate Questions to Focus Research
(See Student Text, pages 348 and 355)

Make note of historical figures from the Renaissance, the Reformation, and the Scientific Revolution whom you might like to research. Make note of the movement with which each person is associated, and write three research questions for each figure. At the end of Lesson 2, circle the individual whom you plan to research.

Historical Figures	Movement	Research Questions

Lessons 3 and 5 Writing Task: Find and Use Credible Sources
(See Student Text, pages 360 and 376)

On a separate sheet of paper, list page references from the topic where you can find information on the individual you selected. Then, consider your research questions. List three other credible resources you will use to conduct additional research. These may be print or digital.

Lesson 4 Writing Task: Develop a Clear Thesis (See Student Text, page 368)

Using your research questions and your research, answer the question: **How did this individual contribute to the spread of new ideas in Europe?** Write one sentence in response to the question. You will use this response as a basis for your thesis statement. As you gather additional research, you may wish to revise your answer. Then, write your thesis statement.

Rough Response:

Thesis Statement:

Lesson 6 Writing Task: Pick an Organizing Strategy
(See Student Text, page 382)

Consider how you will present the evidence to support your thesis statement. You might present information in chronological order, or you might examine several themes, influences, or effects of the individual's life and work. Then, on a separate sheet of paper, use your notes to prepare an outline. Remember that your paper must have an introduction and a conclusion. It should also include at least one, and no more than three, quotes.

Writing Task (See Student Text, page 385)

Use your thesis statement, evidence, quotes, and outline to answer the following question in a research paper: How did this individual contribute to the spread of new ideas in Europe?

When you have finalized your research paper, prepare a Works Cited page in which you list your sources. Be sure to attribute any quotes that you use.

INTERACTIVE

For extra help, review the 21st Century Tutorials: **Search for Information on the Internet** and **Avoid Plagiarism**.

Global Convergence Preview

Essential Question What are the costs and benefits of human expansion?

Before you begin this topic, think about the Essential Question by completing the following activity.

1. List two positive aspects and two negative aspects of global expansion and contact.

....
.
.
.
.
.
.
.
.
.
....

2. Preview the topic by skimming lesson titles, headings, and graphics. Then place a check mark next to each person you predict will play an important role in global expansion during this era.

__Vasco da Gama	__Prince Henry the Navigator	__George Washington
__Ferdinand Magellan	__Hernán Cortés	__Genghis Khan
__Martin Luther	__Queen Isabella of Spain	

Timeline Skills

As you read, write and/or draw at least three events from the topic. Draw a line from each event to its correct position on the timeline.

. . . .

1400	**1500**

Map Skills

Using maps throughout the topic, label the outline map with the places listed. Then color in areas colonized by the Spanish.

Central America	New Spain	New Granada	Peru
North America	South America	Chile	Cuba
Hispaniola	Puerto Rico		

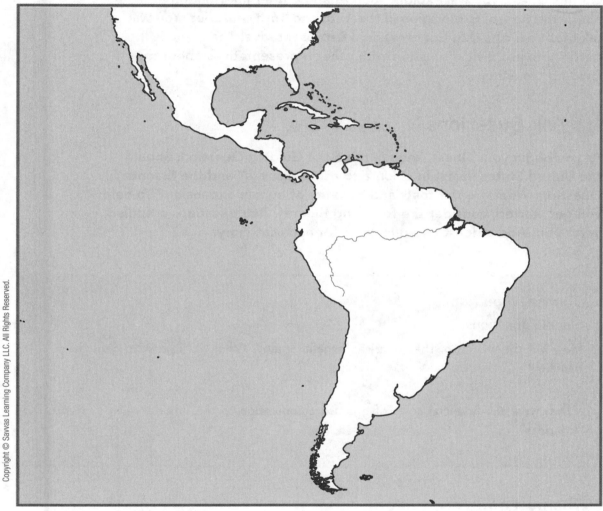

1600　　　　　　1700

Quest

Discussion Inquiry

Colonizing Planets

On this Quest, you will explore sources and gather information about the Age of Exploration in the 15th and 16th centuries. You will take the role of a U.S. Congressional Representative. Then, you will participate in a civic discussion with other representatives about the Guiding Question.

1 Ask Questions (See Student Text, page 390)

As you begin your Quest, keep in mind the Guiding Question: **Should the United States invest in colonizing other planets?** and the Essential Question: **What are the costs and benefits of human expansion?** To help you get started, consider the following themes. Two questions are filled in for you. Add at least two questions for each category.

Theme Wealth

Sample questions:

How did the wealth of the Americas benefit Spain? What did it cost to gain these benefits?

What were the financial costs of Spanish colonization to the original people of the Americas?

Theme Food

Theme Disease

Theme Culture

Theme Technology and Knowledge

Theme My Additional Questions

 INTERACTIVE

For extra help with Step 1, review the 21st Century Skills Tutorial: **Ask Questions**.

2 Investigate

As you read about the Age of Exploration, collect five connections from your text to help you answer the Guiding Question. Three connections are already chosen for you.

Connect to Vasco da Gama

Primary Source Vasco da Gama, Journal (See Student Text, page 399)

Here's a connection! What were the difficulties that Vasco da Gama and other early European sailors faced as they explored the oceans for new trade routes?

What dangers would face colonizers of space? How might they address these dangers?

Connect to Columbus's Voyages

Lesson 1 Explorers Find New Routes (See Student Text, page 394)

Here's another connection! What do you think Ferdinand and Isabella considered to be the costs of supporting Columbus's voyages of discovery? What would they see as the benefits?

What do you think the costs and benefits of Spain's explorations would be to the people of the Americas?

Connect to Portugal's Global Empire

Lesson 4 How Did the Portuguese Empire Decline? (See Student Text, page 418)

Here's another connection! Portugal's colonies faced many enemies and other obstacles. What opposition or obstacles might people of Earth face in colonizing other planets?

How might competition for resources lead to conflict between nations?

It's Your Turn! **Find two more connections. Fill in the title of your connections, then answer the questions. Connections may be images, primary sources, maps, or text.**

Your Choice | Connect to

Location in text

What is the main idea of this connection?

What does it tell about what the United States should consider as it debates colonizing other planets?

Your Choice | Connect to

Location in text

What is the main idea of this connection?

What does it tell about what the United States should consider as it debates colonizing other planets?

3 Examine Primary Sources (See Student Text, page 446)

Examine the primary and secondary sources provided online or from your teacher. Fill in the chart to show how these sources provide further information about the costs and benefits of future colonization of other planets. The first one has been started for you.

Should the United States invest in colonizing other planets?	
Source	**Yes or No? Why?**
"Founding Declaration of the Mars Society"	YES, because we can use comparative planetology to better understand the potential threat of global warming on Earth.
"Would It Be Ethical to Colonize Mars?"	
"Astronauts May Face Long-Term Brain Damage as a Result of Space Travel"	

 INTERACTIVE

For extra help with Step 3, review the 21st Century Skills Tutorial: **Compare Viewpoints.**

 **FINDINGS**

④ Discuss! (See Student Text, page 446)

Now that you have collected information and explored documents about the costs and benefits of human expansion, you are ready to discuss with your fellow Congressional Representatives the Guiding Question: **Should the United States invest in colonizing other planets?** Follow the steps below, using the spaces provided to prepare for your discussion.

You will work with a partner in a small group of representatives. Try to reach consensus, a situation in which everyone is in agreement, on the question. Can you do it?

1. **Prepare Your Arguments** You will be assigned a position on the question, either YES or NO.

My position

Work with your partner to review your Quest notes from the Quest Connections and Quest Sources.

- If you were assigned YES, agree with your partner on what you think were the strongest arguments from the Mars Society.

- If you were assigned NO, agree on what you think were the strongest arguments from Stemwedel and Gallego.

2. **Present Your Position** Those assigned YES will present their arguments and evidence first. As you listen, ask clarifying questions to gain information and understanding.

What is a Clarifying Question?	
These types of questions do not judge the person talking. They are only for the listener to be clear on what he or she is hearing.	
Example: Can you tell me more about that?	**Example:** You said [x]. Am I getting that right?

INTERACTIVE

For extra help with Step 4, review the 21st Century Skills Tutorial: **Participate in a Discussion or Debate.**

While the opposite side speaks, take notes on what you hear in the space below.

> *(blank note-taking area)*

3. **Switch!** Now NO and YES will switch sides. If you argued YES before, now you will argue NO. Work with your same partner and use your notes. Add any arguments and evidence from the clues and sources. Those *now* arguing YES go first.

When both sides have finished, answer the following:

Before I started this discussion with my fellow representatives, my opinion was that the United States	*After* I started this discussion with my fellow representatives, my opinion was that the United States
____should invest in colonizing other planets. ____should not invest in colonizing other planets.	____should invest in colonizing other planets. ____should not invest in colonizing other planets.

4. **Point of View** Do you all agree on the answer to the Guiding Question?

- ——Yes

- ——No

If not, on what points *do* you all agree?

> *(blank answer area)*

Take Notes

Literacy Skills: Identify Cause and Effect Use what you have read to complete the chart. Read the event in the Cause column and write an effect in the Effect column. The first one has been completed for you.

Cause	Effect
Europe wanted to buy goods from Asia and Africa.	Europe sought a sea route to Asia that bypassed the Mediterranean Sea.
Bartolomeu Dias proved that Europeans could reach the Indian Ocean by sailing around the southern tip of Africa.	
Christopher Columbus sailed west to reach the East Indies.	
	Sailors could circumnavigate the globe.
	Sailors chose the best time of year to set sail.

INTERACTIVE

For extra help, review the 21st Century Skills Tutorial: **Analyze Cause and Effect**.

Global Convergence

Practice Vocabulary

Sentence Builder Finish the sentences below with a key term from this section. You may have to change the form of the words to complete the sentences.

Word Bank

missionary   cartography   caravel   circumnavigate

1. European-built vessels with triangular sails and two or three masts are called

2. To sail completely around the world is to

3. The science of creating globes and maps is known as

4. People who attempt to convert others to a specific religion are known as

Quick Activity A Memorable Map

With a partner or small group, examine the nautical chart below.

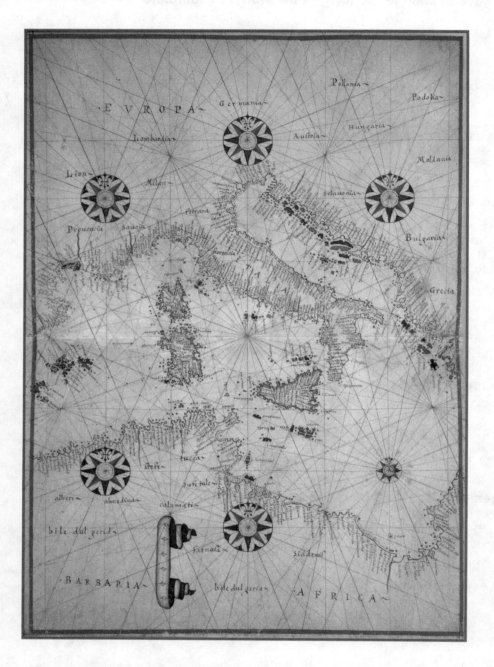

The technology of cartography has changed significantly over the past several hundred years, causing nautical charts to be more comprehensive and accurate. What advantages and disadvantages can you imagine for these new navigation tools?

Team Challenge! Draw a map of your school or area of your school. Include and label important details. Post the map in your classroom. Take a gallery walk to view everyone's ideas to see how the same idea can be mapped in different ways.

Take Notes

Literacy Skills: Sequence Use what you have read to complete the flowchart. In each space write an event to show how the Spanish conquered the Aztec Empire. The first one has been completed for you.

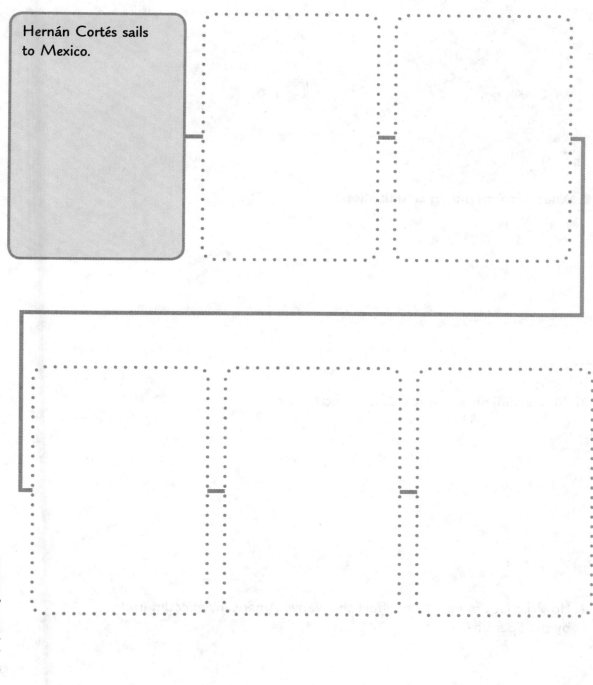

Hernán Cortés sails to Mexico.

INTERACTIVE

For extra help, review the 21st Century Skills Tutorial: **Sequence**.

Practice Vocabulary

Words in Context For each question below, write an answer that shows your understanding of the boldfaced key term.

1. Who were the **conquistadors**?

2. What happens during **colonization**?

3. What is **bullion** and why was it valued?

4. How did lack of **immunity** affect the Native Americans encountered by the Spanish?

Take Notes

Literacy Skills: Identify Main Idea and Details Use what you have read to complete the table. In each space write four details under the correct main idea. The first one has been started for you.

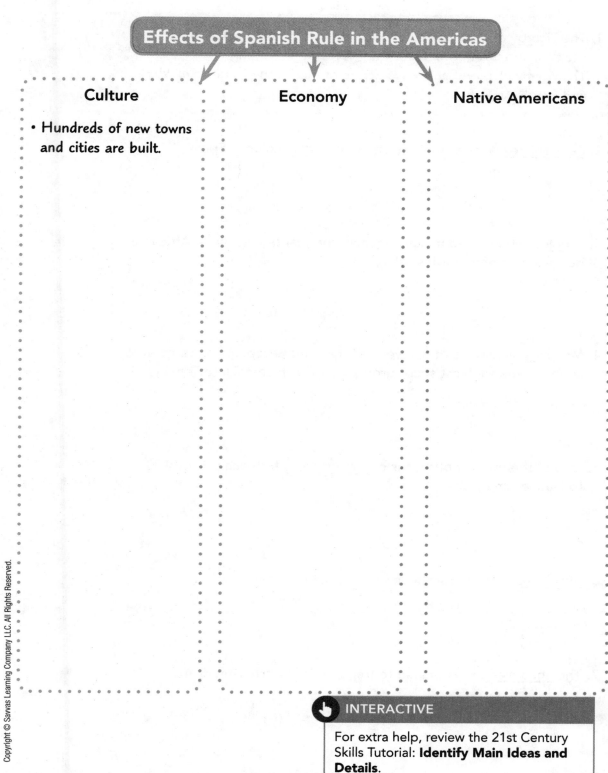

Effects of Spanish Rule in the Americas

Culture	Economy	Native Americans
• Hundreds of new towns and cities are built.		

INTERACTIVE

For extra help, review the 21st Century Skills Tutorial: **Identify Main Ideas and Details**.

Practice Vocabulary

Sentence Revision Revise each sentence so that the underlined vocabulary word is used logically. Be sure not to change the vocabulary word. The first one is done for you.

1. The <u>viceroy</u> of New Spain conquered territories in the Caribbean, Mexico, and South America.
   The <u>viceroy</u> of New Spain governed territories in the Caribbean, Mexico, and South America.

2. <u>Peninsulares</u> were at the bottom of society in colonial Spain.

3. <u>Creoles</u>, who owned mines, ranches, and plantations, were African-born descendants of Spanish settlers.

4. <u>Mestizos</u>, who were of Native American and European descent, were among the wealthiest social groups in Spanish colonial society.

5. One of the primary purposes of <u>missions</u> was to teach sailing skills to Native Americans.

6. <u>Mulattoes</u> were of European and Mexican descent.

7. The <u>encomienda</u> system led to freedom for Native Americans.

Take Notes

Literacy Skills: Analyze Text Structure Use what you have read to complete the outline. Add details to explain the significance of Portuguese colonization during this era. The first entries are completed for you.

Significance of Portuguese Colonization

I. Brazil

    A. Politics and Wealth

        1. Portugal aimed to challenge Spain's position as the most powerful country in Europe, and Brazil's wealth would finance further colonial expansion.

        2. 4 million enslaved Africans brought to work; a new culture emerged blending European, Native American, African influences.

    B. Colonization Effect on Native Americans

        1. Death and illness were widespread since little immunity to European diseases.

        2. Portuguese converted many native people to Christianity.

II. Asia

    A.

        1.

    B.

        1.

        2.

III. Decline of the Portuguese Empire

    A.

        1.

        2.

        3.

 INTERACTIVE

For extra help, review the 21st Century Skills Tutorial: **Identify Main Ideas and Details**.

Practice Vocabulary

Matching Logic Using your knowledge of the underlined vocabulary words, draw a line from each sentence in Column 1 to match it with the sentence in Column 2 to which it logically belongs.

Column 1	Column 2
1. <u>Privateers</u> attacked cargo ships from the Americas.	Illegal smuggling was frequent in the colonies.
2. Early settlers discovered an important export—<u>brazilwood</u>.	This brought cinnamon, pepper, and other seasonings to European markets.
3. The <u>spice trade</u> was very profitable for Portugal and other countries.	The pope wanted to divide the non-European world between Spain and Portugal.
4. The <u>Treaty of Tordesillas</u> decided the location and terms of the <u>Line of Demarcation</u>.	The Portuguese named the South American colony after a tree which produced a valuable reddish-purple dye.

Take Notes

Literacy Skills: Summarize Use what you have read to complete the chart. In each space write details that elaborate on the main idea, then write a summary below. One detail has been entered for you.

Columbian Exchange	European Economy	Ming Dynasty
		Hongwu Emperor stimulated agricultural production.

Summary

👆 INTERACTIVE

For extra help, review the 21st Century Skills Tutorial: **Summarize**.

Practice Vocabulary

True or False? Decide whether each statement below is true or false. Circle T or F, and then explain your answer. Be sure to include the underlined vocabulary word in your explanation. The first one is done for you.

1. **T / F** The <u>Columbian Exchange</u> is the exchange of people, other living things, and ideas between the Eastern and Western hemispheres.
True; The <u>Columbian Exchange</u> mainly took place across the Atlantic Ocean between the Americas, Europe, Asia, and Africa.

2. **T / F** The economic policy of <u>mercantilism</u> promotes the expansion of trade as a means of strengthening a nation.

3. **T / F** Under the economic system of <u>capitalism</u>, businesses are owned by the government.

4. **T / F** <u>Inflation</u> occurs when there is an increase in available cash and a decrease in prices.

5. **T / F** In a <u>traditional economy</u>, the exchange of goods is based on custom.

6. **T / F** People engaged in <u>cottage industries</u> worked long hours in factories.

7. **T / F** In a <u>market economy</u>, competition affects prices and the distribution of goods.

Take Notes

Literacy Skills: Compare and Contrast Use what you have read to complete the Venn diagram. In each space write details that describe Jamestown, Plymouth, or both colonies. The first one has been started for you.

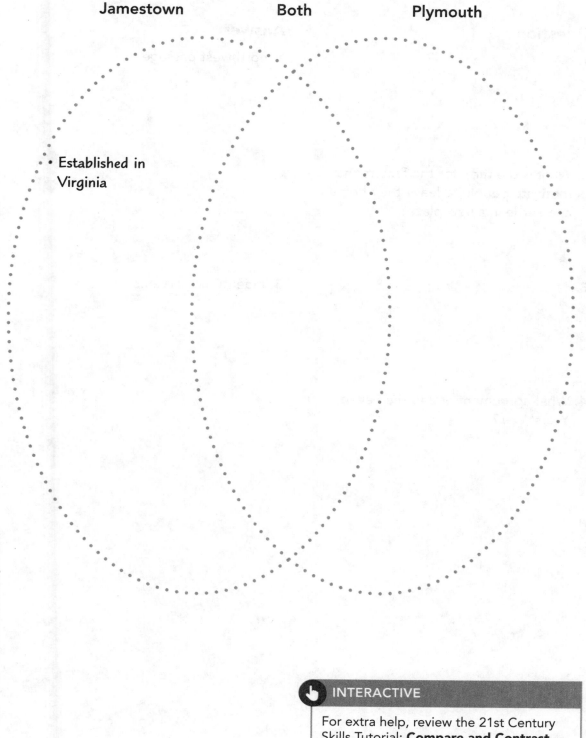

Jamestown   Both   Plymouth

- Established in Virginia

INTERACTIVE

For extra help, review the 21st Century Skills Tutorial: **Compare and Contrast**.

Practice Vocabulary

Vocabulary Quiz Show Some quiz shows ask a question and expect the contestant to give the answer. In other shows, the contestant is given an answer and must supply the question. If the blank is in the Question column, write the question that would result in the answer in the Answer column. If the question is supplied, write the answer.

Question	Answer
1.	1. northwest passage
2. What is the term for the factors that motivate people to leave their homes and settle in a new place?	2.
3.	3. indentured servants
4. What agreement ended the Seven Years' War?	4.

Take Notes

Literacy Skills: Integrate Visual Information Use what you have read to complete the table. Write three visual elements from the lesson in the first column, the main message of each visual element in the second column, and whether the visual element adds, clarifies, or repeats information presented in the text in the third column. One has been completed for you.

Visual Element	Main Idea	Adds, Clarifies, or Repeats Information
People from Burkino Faso making music, page 153	To show the survival of African culture in the face of slavery	Adds information

Select one visual element and explain why you think the author included the visual instead of simply using text to convey the message.

INTERACTIVE

For extra help, review the 21st Century Skills Tutorials: **Synthesize** and **Draw Conclusions**.

Practice Vocabulary

Use a Word Bank Choose one word from the word bank to fill in each blank. When you have finished, you will have a short summary of important ideas from the section.

Word Bank

chattel   Middle Passage   triangular trade   mutiny

The international trade network known as the :................................:

was formed by a three-way group of trade routes that crossed the Atlantic

Ocean. These three routes linked Europe, Africa, and the Americas. On

the first part of the journey, merchants shipped cloth and other goods

from Europe to Africa. On the second part of the journey, called the

:................................:, African captives were sent across the

ocean to the Americas to be sold into slavery. Then, during the final

part of the journey, colonial products were sent to Europe. The enslaved

Africans, considered :................................:, had no rights.

However, fearful of a :................................:, the men operating

the slave ships would chain the male captives together.

Quick Activity The Middle Passage

With a partner or small group, read the following quotes.

> "The closeness of the place, and the heat of the climate, added to the number in the ship, which was so crowded that each had scarcely room to turn himself, almost suffocated us."
>
> — Olaudah Equiano, *The Interesting Narrative of the Life of Olaudah Equiano, or Gustavus Vassa, the African* (1815)

> "The [Africans] were chained to each other hand and foot, and stowed so close, that they were not allowed above a foot and a half for each in breadth."
>
> —Sir William Dolben, British Member of Parliament who proposed an act to regulate conditions on slave ships

Team Challenge! After Dolben's Act of 1788, British abolitionists, including Olaudah Equiano, continued to fight against the slave trade and the institution of slavery. In 1807, the slave trade was outlawed in the British empire, and in 1833, slavery was abolished in the empire. With your partner or group, put yourself in the place of a British citizen in 1805. Write a letter to your member of Parliament asking them to end the slave trade and slavery itself.

Writing Workshop Arguments

As you read, build a response to this question: **Was the impact of global convergence mostly positive or mostly negative?** The prompts below will help walk you through the process.

Lesson 1 Writing Task: Introduce Claims (See Student Text, page 398)

Write one sentence stating your opinion of the impact of global convergence. This will be your claim for the argument you will write at the end of the topic.

Lesson 2 Writing Task: Support Claims (See Student Text, page 405)

List important facts and examples from the text that support or oppose your claim.

Support Claim	Oppose Claim

Global Convergence

Lesson 3 Writing Task: Distinguish Claims from Opposing Claims
(See Student Text, page 412)

Write three sentences explaining how your claims are different from opposing claims.

> (blank response box)

Lesson 4 Writing Task: Use Credible Sources (See Student Text, page 419)

Think about credible sources from which you could gather additional evidence on global convergence. On a separate piece of paper, list these sources as well as the evidence each one provides.

Lessons 5 and 6 Writing Task: Shape Tone (See Student Text, pages 430 and 438)

Review your main claim statement. Consider your audience and adjust the tone of your statement as necessary. Clarify relationships between your claim and the evidence by using transition words such as *for example, for instance, specifically, because, consequently, therefore, thus,* and *as a result.*

> (blank response box)

Lesson 7 Writing Task: Write a Conclusion (See Student Text, page 445)

Review your claim and evidence. Write a strong conclusion sentence to concisely sum up your argument on the impact of global convergence.

> (blank response box)

Writing Task (See Student Text, page 447)

Using the evidence you have gathered, write a five-paragraph essay arguing your claim. Your claim should be clear and supported by the evidence you have gathered.

TOPIC 10 Absolutism and Enlightenment Preview

Essential Question What is the best form of government?

Before you begin this topic, think about the Essential Question by completing the following activity.

1. What does it mean to you to be governed or have rules and laws?

2. Preview the topic by skimming lesson titles, headlines, and graphics. Place a check mark next to qualities that you predict will be true of European governments in the years leading up to the Enlightenment.

__powerful   __kind   __religious   __fair

__tolerant   __peaceful   __absolute   __wealthy

__democratic

Timeline Skills

As you read, write and/or draw at least three events from the topic. Draw a line from each event to its correct position on the timeline.

1500	1600

Map Skills

Using maps throughout the topic, label the outline map with the places listed. Then, color in the water.

Russia	Spain	England	Sweden
Austria	Poland	Prussia	France
Norway	Ottoman Empire	Mediterranean Sea	Baltic Sea

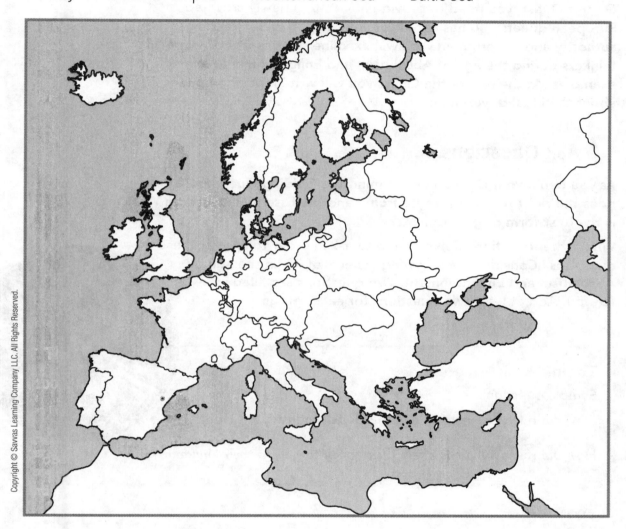

1700   1800

Quest
Document-Based Writing Inquiry

The Right to Rule

On this Quest, you need to provide advice to a newly crowned European queen who has asked for your help in understanding authority and government. You will examine sources from European thinkers during the age of Absolutism and Enlightenment to find examples. At the end of the Quest you will write a position paper about the ideal government.

1 Ask Questions (See Student Text, page 452)

As you begin your Quest, keep in mind the Guiding Question: **Where does the right to govern come from?** and the Essential Question: **What is the best form of government?**

What other questions do you need to ask in order to answer these questions? Consider the following aspects of life in the age of Absolutism and Enlightenment. Two questions are filled in for you. Add at least two questions for each category.

Theme Religion and the Church

Sample questions:

How did rulers use religion and the church to justify their rule?

How did rulers' religions affect their ability to govern their kingdoms?

Theme Science, Art, and Humanism

Theme Government and the People

Theme Trade and Warfare

Theme My Additional Questions

 INTERACTIVE

For extra help with Step 1, review the
21st Century Tutorial: **Ask Questions**.

② Investigate

As you read about Absolutism and Enlightenment, collect five connections from your text to help you answer the Guiding Question. Three are already chosen for you.

Connect to Bishop Jacques Bossuet

Primary Source Jacques Bossuet, *Politics Drawn from the Very Words of Holy Scripture* (See Student Text, page 462)

Here's a connection! What does this Primary Source tell you about where Bishop Jacques Bossuet believed the right to govern comes from?

How do you think this works in practice?

Connect to John Locke

Primary Source John Locke, *Two Treatises of Government*
(See Student Text, page 482)

Here's another connection! What are John Locke's ideas about authority and the social contract?

How do you think these ideas affected Europe and the rulers who governed?

Connect to Baron de Montesquieu

Analysis Skills Draw Sound Conclusions from Sources
(See Student Text, page 483)

What does this connection reveal about Montesquieu's concept of authority?

What impact did this idea have on the history of the world?

It's Your Turn! **Find two more connections. Fill in the title of your connections, then answer the questions. Connections may be images, primary sources, maps, or text.**

Your Choice | Connect to

Location in text

What is the main idea of this connection?

What does it tell you about the ideal government or the right to rule?

Your Choice | Connect to

Location in text

What is the main idea of this connection?

What does it tell you about the ideal government or the right to rule?

3 **Examine Primary Sources** (See Student Text, page 484)

Examine the primary and secondary sources provided online or from your teacher. Fill in the chart to show how these sources provide further information about where the right to govern comes from. The first one is completed for you.

Source	Explanation
Leviathan	In Leviathan, Thomas Hobbes explains that citizens should enter a social contract with an absolute ruler, because giving that ruler complete authority is the only true way to ensure protection and order.
Patriarcha	
The Social Contract	
Divine Right of Kings	
The Sun King	

INTERACTIVE

For extra help with Step 3, review the 21st Century Tutorials: **Analyze Primary and Secondary Sources** and **Analyze Images**.

4 Write Your Position Paper (See Student Text, page 484)

Now it's time to put together all of the information you have gathered and use it to write your argument. Absolute monarchs and Enlightenment thinkers had different ideas about where the right to govern comes from, as well as what those rights are, and who should have them. Use the steps below to outline your position on this issue and complete the writing process.

1. **Prepare to Write** You have collected connections and explored primary sources to learn more about where the right to govern comes from. On a separate piece of paper, summarize your position on this issue in one sentence. This will become the thesis statement for your argument.

2. **Outline Your Argument** Look through your notes for evidence that supports your thesis statement. Use the table below to begin to outline your argument.

Introduction Your thesis	
Evidence From primary sources	
Additional Evidence From primary sources	
Conclusion Restatement of your thesis	

3. **Write a Draft** Write a draft of your argument using your outline. Add transitional words and phrases to strengthen your argument and clarify your position.

4. **Share with a Partner** With a partner, correct any grammatical, spelling, or factual errors and make sure that your argument makes sense.

5. **Finalize Your Paper** Finalize your argument and use technology to publish your paper.

6. **Reflect on the Quest** Think about your experience in completing this topic's Quest. What did you learn about the different ideas about rights and where the right to govern comes from? What questions do you still have about absolute monarchs and the Enlightenment? How will you answer them?

Reflections

 INTERACTIVE

For extra help with Step 5, review the 21st Century Tutorial: **Publish Your Work**.

Take Notes

Literacy Skill: Cite Evidence Use what you have read to complete the table. Draw conclusions from the text, and support these statements with three pieces of evidence. One conclusion has been provided for you. Add evidence to support the conclusion, and then try one on your own.

> Charles V and Philip II were responsible for the golden age of Spain.

> Charles V was hard-working and knew he had to answer to Spanish nobles.

INTERACTIVE

For extra help, review the 21st Century Tutorial: **Support Ideas with Evidence**.

Practice Vocabulary

Sentence Revision Revise each sentence so that the underlined vocabulary word is used logically. Be sure not to the change the vocabulary word. The first one is done for you.

1. The mighty Spanish <u>armada</u> fought many battles on land.
   The mighty Spanish <u>armada</u> fought many battles at sea.

2. As <u>absolute monarch</u>, Louis XIV wanted to share power with his people.

3. The idea of <u>divine right</u> meant that Louis XIV believed the people gave him the right to power.

4. Spanish <u>inflation</u> caused prices for goods and services to decrease.

5. An <u>assassin</u> gave birth to Henry IV.

Take Notes

Literacy Skills: Compare and Contrast Compare and contrast Russian reforms under Peter the Great and Catherine the Great.

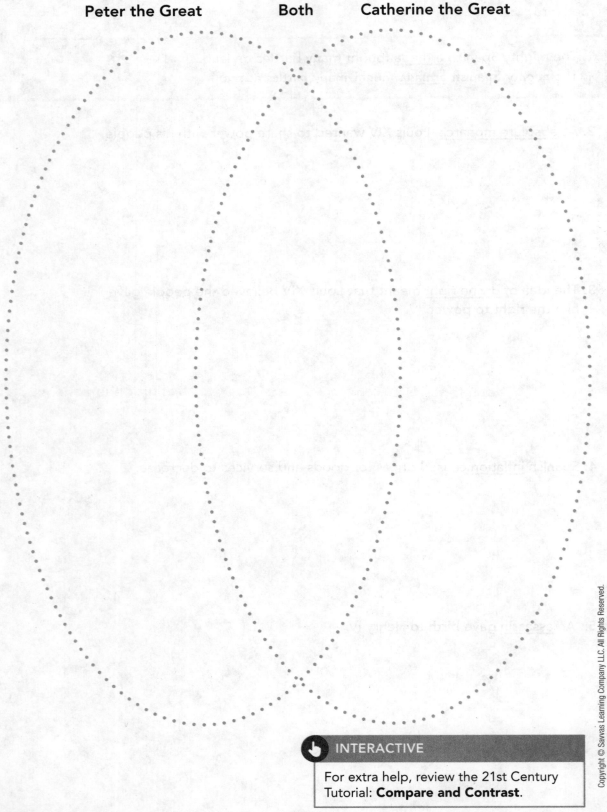

Peter the Great   Both   Catherine the Great

INTERACTIVE

For extra help, review the 21st Century Tutorial: **Compare and Contrast**.

Practice Vocabulary

Word Map Study the word map for the word *tsar*. Characteristics are words or phrases that relate to the word in the center of the word map. Non-characteristics are words and phrases not associated with the word. Use the blank word map to explore the meaning of the word *serf*. Then make your own word map for the word *partition*.

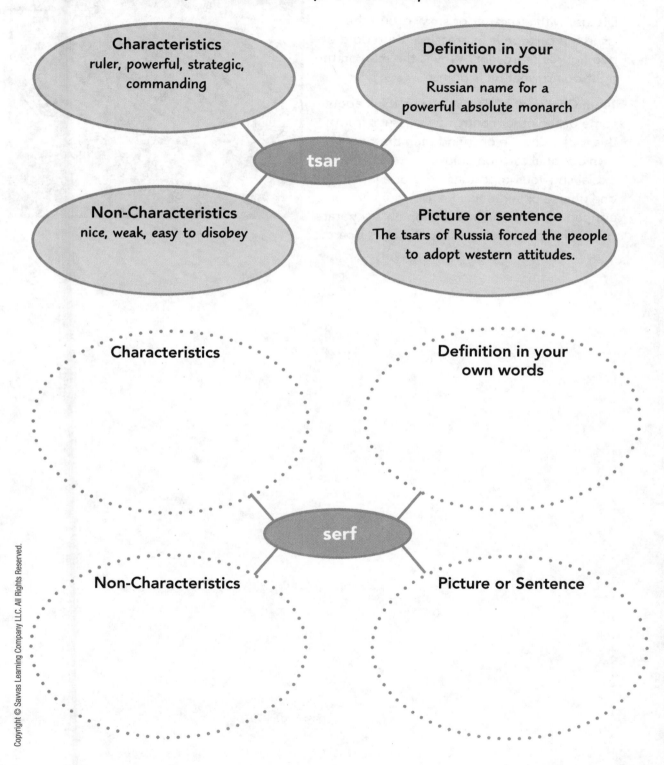

Characteristics
ruler, powerful, strategic, commanding

Definition in your own words
Russian name for a powerful absolute monarch

tsar

Non-Characteristics
nice, weak, easy to disobey

Picture or sentence
The tsars of Russia forced the people to adopt western attitudes.

Characteristics

Definition in your own words

serf

Non-Characteristics

Picture or Sentence

Quick Activity Editorial Cartoon

An editorial cartoon is an illustration that expresses a message, often about a controversial event or issue. Let's take a closer look at the editorial cartoon from your text.

Discuss with a partner or small group the issue the cartoon is expressing. Who do the two figures represent? Why is the man on the right doing what he is doing?

Team Challenge! With a partner, think about some of the other controversial issues from this topic. Choose one, and then draft your own editorial cartoon below. Write a caption explaining your important issue or event in one phrase or sentence. Revise your cartoon as needed, create a final version on a separate piece of paper, and post it to the class board.

Take Notes

Literacy Skills: Identify Cause and Effect Use what you have read to complete the chart. For each effect, identify three causes. The first has been completed for you.

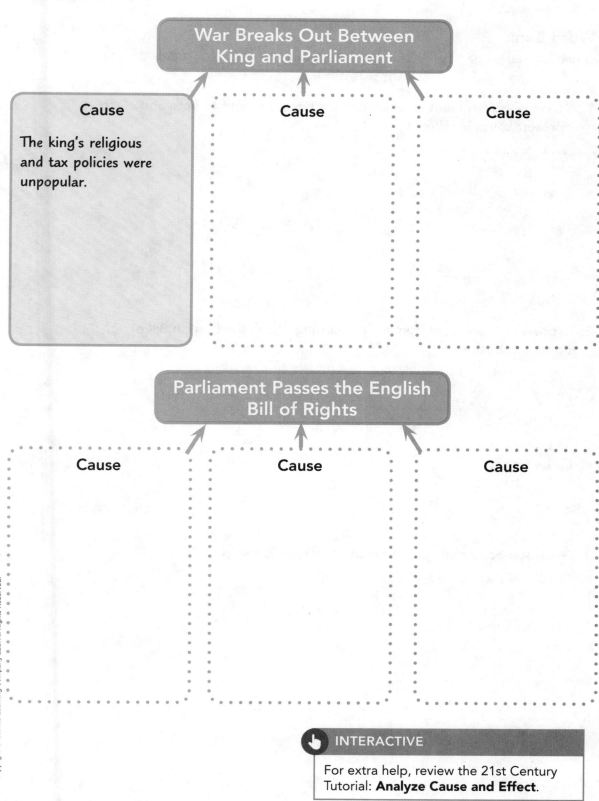

War Breaks Out Between King and Parliament

Cause

The king's religious and tax policies were unpopular.

Cause

Cause

Parliament Passes the English Bill of Rights

Cause

Cause

Cause

INTERACTIVE

For extra help, review the 21st Century Tutorial: **Analyze Cause and Effect**.

Practice Vocabulary

Sentence Builder Finish the sentences below with a key term from this section. You may have to change the form of the word to complete the sentences.

Word Bank

constitutional monarchy   republic   treason

1. A form of government in which citizens have the right to vote and elect representatives is called a

:..:
:   :
:..:

2. To prevent absolutism from ever occurring again, the English Bill of Rights established a

:..:
:   :
:..:

3. When someone betrays their own country, it is called

:......................................:
:   :
:......................................:

Take Notes

Literacy Skills: Summarize Use what you have read to complete the table. Summarize the major ideas that came out of the Enlightenment.

Political Ideas	Social Ideas	Economic Ideas

Summary

👆 **INTERACTIVE**

For extra help, review the 21st Century Tutorial: **Summarize**.

Practice Vocabulary

Matching Logic Using your knowledge of the underlined vocabulary words, draw a line from each sentence in Column 1 to match it with the sentence in Column 2 to which it logically belongs.

Column 1	Column 2
1. Voltaire argued that Christians should demonstrate <u>tolerance</u>.	If a government fails to protect them, the people should rebel and form a new government.
2. Montesquieu believed in <u>separation of powers</u>.	People agree to give up unlimited freedom in exchange for protection of their liberties.
3. John Locke believed that <u>natural rights</u> belong to all people.	Allowing others to hold beliefs different from one's own is essential for peace.
4. Many Enlightenment thinkers believed that a <u>social contract</u> was the basis of any government.	Having a legislative, judicial, and executive branch establishes a system of checks and balances.

Quick Activity In Your Own Words

Examine the quotes below from the Magna Carta, English Bill of Rights, and the Declaration of Independence. Discuss with a partner the similarities and differences between the quotes.

"(39) No free man shall be seized or imprisoned, or stripped of his rights or possessions, or outlawed or exiled or deprived of his standing in any way, nor will we proceed with force against him, or send others to do so, except by the lawful judgment of his equals or by the law of the land."

—*Magna Carta (1215)*

"The pretended power of dispensing with laws or the execution of laws by regal authority, as it hath been assumed and exercised of late, is illegal."

—*English Bill of Rights*

"We hold these truths to be self-evident that all men are created equal, that they are endowed by their Creator with certain unalienable Rights, that among these are Life, Liberty, and the pursuit of Happiness."

—*U.S. Declaration of Independence*

Team Challenge! With your partner, choose one of the quotes and rewrite the idea in your own words. Then, share your rewrite with the class.

Writing Workshop Arguments

As you read, build a response to this question: **Was the concept of an absolute monarchy doomed?** The prompts below will help walk you through the process.

Lesson 1 Writing Task: Introduce Claims (See Student Text, page 461)

Write a sentence that introduces your opinion about the question of whether or not the concept of absolute monarchy was doomed. This opinion will become the thesis statement of the argument that you will write at the end of the topic.

Lesson 2 Writing Task: Support Claims (See Student Text, page 467)

Now add details from the lessons to support your claim.

Lesson 1:	
Lesson 2:	
Lesson 3:	
Lesson 4:	